Saskatchewan TRIVIA Challenge

Robin and Arlene Karpan

D0974259

PARKLAND
PUBLISHING

Saskatoon

Second printing 2001
Third printing and updating 2003

Published in Canada in 2000 by
Parkland Publishing
501 Mount Allison Place
Saskatoon, Saskatchewan
Canada S7H 4A9

Telephone: (306) 242-7731
e-mail: info@parklandpublishing.com
web site: www.parklandpublishing.com

Printed in Canada by Houghton Boston, Saskatoon.

Canadian Cataloguing in Publication Data

Karpan, Robin.

Saskatchewan trivia challenge

ISBN 0-9683579-2-X

1. Saskatchewan – Miscellanea.   I. Karpan, Arlene.
I. Title.

FC3511.6.K37 2000   971.24′002   C00-920118-1
F1071.5.K37 2000

Preface

This book grew out of our continuing fascination with where we live. Almost everywhere we travelled in Saskatchewan, there seemed to be a claim to fame – historical happenings, unique landscapes, homes of famous folks, or larger than life monuments ranging from attractive to odd to completely off-the-wall (well, in one case it actually is a wall). The further we looked, the more surprises we discovered. A lot has happened in Saskatchewan, and continues to happen, from momentous events in history and politics to achievements in sports, agriculture, industry or the arts.

Saskatchewan Trivia Challenge is not only about Saskatchewan's biggest, best, firsts and other superlatives. The tidbits of curious, obscure or frivolous facts are often just as intriguing.

Numerous people assisted us in researching and fact checking the questions, and providing photos. To the many representatives of organizations and communities, we extend our thanks.

Saskatchewan Trivia Challenge was the proud recipient of the Souvenir of the Year Award in the 2000 Saskatchewan Tourism Awards of Excellence.

Contents

In the Beginning 5
Pages from the Past 11
Working the Land 37
The Wheat Province? 45
Furthermore, If I Get Elected 50
Doing Business 64
Sweeeeep! 72
The Olympians 76
Football Fever 79
The Puck Stops Here 84
World's Greatest Swingers 87
Lay of the Land 90
Lakes and Rivers 96
On the Wild Side 106
A Peek at Parks 120
Readin' and Writin' 124
The Entertainers 129
Weathering the Storm 135
Gone Fishin' 142
Bricks and Mortar 148
Flying High 159
Bridging the Gap 165
Monumental Musings 171
Official Stuff 184

In the Beginning

Question

How old are Saskatchewan's oldest fossils?

a) 170,000 years old
b) 1,700,000 years old
c) 17,000,000 years old
d) 170,000,000 years old
e) 1,700,000,000 years old

Answer

e) The oldest fossils in the province date back 1,700,000,000 years. Known as stromatolites, they are microscopic cells of blue-green algae found in extensive seas that once covered the province.

The Royal Saskatchewan Museum in Regina has a large specimen of these fossilized algae colonies found near Uranium City.

Question

The earliest evidence of people living in what is now Saskatchewan dates back how many years?

a) 1,000 years ago
b) 3,000 years ago
c) 5,000 years ago
d) 7,000 years ago
e) 10,000 years ago

Answer

e) A campfire hearth, associated with debris from stone tool manufacturing, has been radiocarbon-dated at approximately 10,000 years old. Found near Ponteix and known as the Napao Site, this is the oldest dated archaeological site in Saskatchewan.

The second oldest is the Heron Eden Site near Prelate where two stone spear tips were found in direct association with the bones of several large bison, indicating that bison were killed and butchered here approximately 9,000 years ago.

It is quite possible that people lived here even earlier. Stone projectile points and other tools have been found in Saskatchewan which are similar to types found at sites dated to 10,000 years and earlier on the American Plains. However, surface finds cannot be dated. Archaeologists rely primarily on radiocarbon-dating organic remains in order to date associated artifacts and other physical evidence of human activity. This requires excavation of buried remains. Archaeologists indicate that further excavation will likely reveal more evidence of human life dating back at least 10,000 years and possibly more.

The Heron Eden archaeological site.   Saskatchewan Archaeological Society

Question

Where were the first dinosaur bones discovered in western Canada?

a) Cypress Hills
b) Eastend
c) Rockglen
d) Killdeer Badlands
e) Big Muddy Badlands

Answer

d) The first dinosaur bones in western Canada were found by George Mercer Dawson in 1874 in the Killdeer Badlands south of Wood Mountain. Dawson was a geologist working with the Boundary Commission which was responsible for surveying the 49th parallel, the then unmarked boundary between Canada and the USA. Some of the fossils Dawson collected were bones from *Hadrosaurs* or duck-billed dinosaurs.

Question

In 1994, a major discovery was made near Eastend when the 65-million-year-old remains of a dinosaur dubbed "Scotty" were found. What type of dinosaur is Scotty?

a) *Hadrosaur*
b) *Albertosaurus*
c) *Triceratops*
d) *Corythosaurus*
e) *Tyrannosaurus rex*

Answer

e) Scotty is a *Tyrannosaurus rex*. This was the first *T. rex* skeleton found in Saskatchewan, and one of very few in the world. Scientists indicate that the skeleton is about 65% complete, and that about 30 of its 60 razor-sharp teeth have been found.

T. rex, whose name means "king of the lizards" was the largest meat-eating dinosaur that existed. A massive predator weighing as much as six tonnes, *T. rex* measured as long as 13.5 metres (44 feet). It stood on two powerful legs, had a long tail, and two small forelimbs that were too short to reach its mouth. Its teeth ranged in length from 3-28 cm (1.2-11 inches).

The T. rex Discovery Centre in Eastend has displays on Scotty and other significant fossil finds in the area.

Question

In 1995, scientists working near Eastend made a major discovery – the first known "coprolite" belonging to a *Tyrannosaurus rex* dinosaur. What is "coprolite"?

Answer

The news scoop was a big pile of poop! Staff from the Royal Saskatchewan Museum discovered the unusually large piece of dung, weighing 7 kg (over 15 pounds) and measuring 44 cm (17 inches) long, 15 cm (6 inches) high and 13 cm (5 inches) wide.

The discovery was significant because it was the first coprolite or fossilized dropping found in the world that came from a carnivorous dinosaur. By analyzing the contents, scientists gained a better insight into how the giant meat-eater consumed food. *T. rex* did not have any molars, and could not move its jaw from side to side to chew, therefore it was previously believed that it ate by nibbling the flesh of its prey and swallowing large pieces. However, when they found fragments of bones from a smaller dinosaur in the coprolite, scientists learned that *T. rex* was capable of shattering large thick bones with its powerful jaws.

T. rex *droppings (coprolite).*   Royal Saskatchewan Museum Photo

9

Question

Where was "Big Bert", the 92-million-year-old crocodile, found?

a) South Saskatchewan River
b) North Saskatchewan River
c) Carrot River
d) Assiniboine River
e) Frenchman River

Answer

c) The fossilized remains of "Big Bert" were discovered in 1991 on the banks of the Carrot River. Researchers identified the remains as *Teleorhinus*, a rare species of crocodile that lived 92 million years ago. The crocodile had a long slender snout that enabled it to catch fish, and a powerful tail that would have helped it move through the water. One of only four specimens in North America, and the only one in Canada, "Big Bert" measured 7 metres (23 feet) long.

The skeleton was removed in 1991 and 1992 and taken to the Royal Saskatchewan Museum in Regina for further study. Each summer at Pasquia Regional Park, a scale model of Big Bert's impressive head is on display. The Andy Jamault Nature Trail in the regional park takes you along the Carrot River to where the remains of Big Bert were unearthed on a shale cliff.

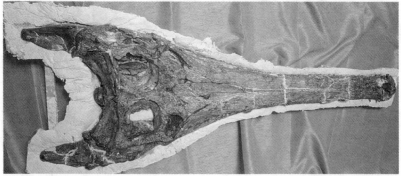

Skull of Big Bert.   Royal Saskatchewan Museum Photo

Pages from the Past

Question ✓

Who was the first European to see the prairies?

a) Alexander Henry
b) Henry Kelsey
c) Alexander Mackenzie
d) Henry Hudson
e) Peter Pond

Answer

b) In 1690-91, Hudson's Bay Company employee Henry Kelsey journeyed inland from York Factory on Hudson Bay in order to encourage Indians of the interior to trade at the Bay's posts.

Historians believe that Kelsey paddled up the Saskatchewan River and explored the Carrot River valley as well as areas around present-day Hudson Bay, Porcupine Plain and Yorkton. Impressed with what he had seen, Kelsey called this the "Inland Country of Good Report". His report of this epic journey is considered the beginning of recorded history in Saskatchewan and western Canada.

Question ✓

Where is the oldest permanent settlement in Saskatchewan?

a) Cumberland House
b) Ile-à-la-Crosse
c) Pelly
d) Battleford
e) Beauval

Answer

a) Cumberland House was established in 1774 by Samuel Hearne who was sent by the Hudson's Bay Company to build its first inland trading post. The Company was concerned that rival fur traders were going directly to Indians of the interior for furs. It was hoped that this new post, built on an island in the Cumberland Delta and near Indian bands and major water routes, would encourage more trade with the Bay.
Cumberland House remained an important centre during the era of the fur trade and northern exploration. It is now a community of about 1,000 residents.

Cumberland House in 1884.

Question ✓

Where was the first permanent Roman Catholic Mission established in Saskatchewan?

a) Cumberland House
b) St. Laurent
c) Ile-à-la-Crosse
d) Stanley Mission
e) Green Lake

Answer

c) The mission of St. John the Baptist at Ile-à-la-Crosse was founded in 1846 by M. Louis Laflêche and Fr. Alexandre Taché.

Ile-à-la-Crosse, 1860.   Saskatchewan Archives R-A 24431

Question

Where was Saskatchewan's only "naval battle"?

Answer

Batoche. To call it a "naval battle" may be stretching things a bit, but it was a military attack involving a boat. In the 1885 Northwest Rebellion, Canadian militia leader General Middleton devised a plan to capture Batoche from Louis Riel's Métis. The steamboat *Northcote* was reinforced with planks and bags of feed. With rifle-toting soldiers aboard, the steamer would be sent downriver to Batoche as a diversion, while Middleton's forces attacked overland from the south.

As the *Northcote* chugged into range, Riel's men rushed to the river to fire at the passing "gunboat". It seems Middleton hadn't accounted for the ferry cable stretched across the river. The *Northcote's* tall smokestacks hit the cable and came crashing down. The captain hit the deck to avoid the hail of bullets as the boat drifted helplessly downstream. The soldiers aboard wanted to turn around and go back to Batoche, but the *Northcote's* civilian captain had had enough of this nonsense and guided the boat downstream out of harm's way.

The *Northcote* did cause a diversion, but to no avail, as Middleton's men arrived too late. With Saskatchewan's only "gunboat" out of the way, the Métis were able to get back to the rifle pits to try to defend Batoche from advancing troops.

Artist's sketch of the Northcote *at Batoche, appearing in the* Canadian Pictorial and Illustrated War News, *1885.* Saskatchewan Archives R-B 7380

Question ✓

Where did Canada's largest mass execution take place?

a) Prince Albert penitentiary
b) RCMP headquarters at Regina
c) Fort Battleford
d) Saskatoon
e) Fort Walsh

Answer

c) In November, 1885, eight Indians were hanged at Fort Battleford for murders committed at Frog Lake, Fort Pitt, and Battleford during the Northwest Rebellion. Among those executed was Wandering Spirit, who was a leader in the Frog Lake killings which left nine dead. The gallows was specially designed so that all eight dropped at once. The bodies were then buried in a common grave overlooking the North Saskatchewan River, not far from Fort Battleford. The hangman was Robert Hodson, one of those taken prisoner by Wandering Spirit's men at Fort Pitt.

Question ✓

Where was the first permanent capital of the North-West Territories?

a) Fort Carlton
b) Battleford
c) Regina
d) Fort Livingstone
e) Fort Walsh

Answer

b) When the North-West Territories Act was proclaimed in 1876, Battleford was declared the capital, due to its central location. However, before the lieutenant governor and his councillors could take up office in Battleford, suitable buildings had to be constructed. The North-West Territories Council first met at Fort Livingstone (near present-day Pelly) in 1877, and moved to Battleford in 1878 after the new buildings were completed. In 1883, the capital was moved to Regina.

Battleford's Government House.   Karpan Photo

Question

This famous portage route played a key role in the fur trade because it connected rivers flowing to Hudson Bay with rivers flowing to the Arctic Ocean:

a) Portage La Loche (Methye Portage)
b) Camsell Portage
c) Pemmican Portage
d) Frog Portage
e) Cranberry Portage

Answer

a) Portage La Loche, also known as Methye Portage, is a 20-kilometre portage across the height of land between Lac La Loche and the Clearwater River in northwest Saskatchewan.

The portage was an important land bridge because it provided a link between eastern-flowing waterways such as the Churchill River (connected to Lac La Loche) that empty into Hudson Bay, and the Clearwater that flows into the Athabasca River, and is part of the Arctic Ocean drainage system.

Peter Pond was the first white man to cross the portage in 1778, opening up the huge Athabasca region to the lucrative fur trade.

At first, voyageurs carried their boats, supplies and furs across the portage. In the mid-1820s, a more practical system was developed. Brigades left their York boats at one end of the portage, carried their goods across, and loaded boats waiting at the other end. Pack horses and ox-carts were used about 30 years later, greatly increasing the volume of goods and furs transported.

Question

Where were the first shots fired in the Northwest Rebellion of 1885?

a) Duck Lake
b) Fish Creek
c) Batoche
d) Clark's Crossing
e) Frog Lake

Answer

a) The first shots were fired just west of Duck Lake on March 26, 1885. Gabriel Dumont and a number of Louis Riel's supporters had taken control of Duck Lake, where a store contained guns and provisions. On March 26, Superintendent Crozier led North West Mounted Police from Fort Carlton and civilian volunteers from Prince Albert to face the Métis. Negotiations took place, but a scuffle broke out. It is believed

that the first shot was fired by "Gentleman" Joe McKay, a Prince Albert volunteer. Hearing the shot, Crozier ordered his men to fire.

The Métis took shelter in an abandoned log building. Crozier's men tried to rush the Métis, but became bogged down in the deep snow. Crozier retreated after about half an hour of fighting, and returned to Fort Carlton. Nine volunteers and three NWMP officers were killed, while the Métis lost five men including Isidore Dumont, Gabriel Dumont's brother.

"Gentleman" Joe McKay.
Saskatchewan Archives R-A 4543

Question

The son of this famous English author became a North West Mounted Police inspector, and played a role in the 1885 Northwest Rebellion:

a) Charles Dickens
b) Robert Louis Stevenson
c) Rudyard Kipling
d) George Bernard Shaw
e) Sir Arthur Conan Doyle

Answer

a) Charles Dickens' third son, Francis Jeffrey Dickens, became commander of a small detachment of Mounted Police at Fort Pitt in northwest Saskatchewan. In the spring of 1885, violence erupted when members of Cree Chief Big Bear's band killed nine residents of the village of Frog Lake, an incident which became known as the Frog Lake Massacre. Two weeks later, the Cree threatened to attack or burn Fort Pitt unless the police left. After negotiations and skirmishes, Dickens and his men finally agreed to abandon the fort. The police loaded their leaky scow, and in a spring snowstorm, floated down the ice-choked North Saskatchewan River to Battleford. After the civilians were taken captive, Fort Pitt was looted then burned.

Insp. Dickens at Ft. Pitt (front with beard).   Saskatchewan Archives R-A 1083

Question

With which performing show group did Gabriel Dumont appear after he fled Canada following the battle at Batoche in May, 1885?

Answer

After fleeing Canada, Dumont appeared as an expert marksman and sharpshooter with Buffalo Bill Cody's Wild West Show. Known as the "Prince of the Plains", Dumont appeared in shows across the United States. In New York, sympathizers to the Métis cause presented Dumont with a gold watch, which is now in the Duck Lake Regional Interpretive Centre.

After the Canadian government declared amnesty for all those who had taken part in the 1885 uprising, Dumont returned to Canada and lived in the Bellevue area near Batoche until his death in 1906. He is buried in the cemetery at Batoche, his

grave marked by a huge triangular-shaped boulder overlooking the South Saskatchewan River.

Gabriel Dumont.

Saskatchewan Archives
R-A 6277

Question

This man is regarded as the founder of the Métis settlement of Batoche. "Batoche" was also his nickname. Who was he?

a) Charles Nolin
b) Bishop Grandin
c) Gabriel Dumont
d) Xavier Letendre
e) Louis Riel

Answer

d) Xavier Letendre is known as the father of Batoche. He started a ferry service and opened a small store to serve Métis settlers in the vicinity. A small village soon grew up around the store and the community became known as Batoche. Letendre is buried in the cemetery at Batoche.

Question

Based on the 1906 census, what was the largest city in Saskatchewan?

a) Regina
b) Saskatoon
c) Moose Jaw
d) Prince Albert
e) North Battleford

Answer

c) Moose Jaw was the largest city with a population of 6,249. Regina was second with 6,169, followed by Saskatoon at 3,011, and Prince Albert at 3,005. The largest town was Indian Head with a population of 1,545, while Yorkton ranked second at 1,363.

Question

The RCMP Musical Ride originated in Saskatchewan. Where did the first ride take place?

a) Fort Walsh
b) Battleford
c) Regina
d) Fort Livingston
e) Wood Mountain Post

Answer

c) The North West Mounted Police (forerunners of the RCMP) staged the first Musical Ride on January 16, 1887 at the newly completed indoor riding school at the Regina barracks. The guest of honor at the performance was Lieutenant Governor Edgar Dewdney.

The origins of the Musical Ride are linked to traditional cavalry drills. Lances, which are cavalry weapons, are carried by each Mountie who is dressed in a Stetson hat, scarlet tunic, riding breeches, brown boots and spurs.

The Musical Ride now consists of 32 specially trained black horses. The horses begin their training at three years of age and begin Musical Ride training when they are six years old. Each performance is a highly coordinated demonstration of precision, skill, and timing.

Question ✓

Saskatoon was founded by John Lake in 1882 with a view to starting a colony. What kind of colony did he have in mind?

a) Barr colony
b) Temperance colony
c) Mennonite colony
d) Hutterite colony
e) Doukhobor colony

Answer

b) John Lake was the leader of the Temperance Colonization Society, dedicated to establishing booze-free colonies in the Canadian west. Lake and a group of settlers arrived at the present site of Saskatoon in 1882 and pronounced it the perfect place for a new teetotaling colony. It was well north of the railway, and thus farther from temptation.

Lake supposedly asked his Cree guide the name of the succulent purple berries growing along the banks of the South Saskatchewan River. Upon being told it was "misaskwatomin", the story goes that Lake jumped to his feet exclaiming "Arise Saskatoon, Queen of the north!"

The colony's utopic dreams were shattered when it became clear that it was impossible to keep liquor away from the settlers. The difficulties were enough to drive a person to drink.

Question

Where was Station #1 on the Outlaw Trail, a route running from Canada to Mexico that was used by Butch Cassidy and the Wild Bunch, along with other cattle and horse thieves?

a) Val Marie
b) Wood Mountain
c) Roche Percee
d) Big Muddy
e) Bienfait

Answer

d) The Big Muddy, near the community of Big Beaver in south-central Saskatchewan, was Station #1 and the only Canadian station on the Outlaw Trail. Set up in the late 1800s, the highly organized escape route wound south to Hole-in-the-Wall in Wyoming, Robber's Roost in Utah, and eventually to Ciudad Juarez, Mexico. Along the way the outlaws could get fresh horses and supplies as well as hide from the law.

The rugged Big Muddy Badlands, with its buttes and deep coulees, made the perfect hideout. It also became the haunt of other cattle and horse thieves such as Dutch Henry and the Nelson-Jones gang. It is still possible to see the caves used by outlaw Sam Kelly; one cave was used by Kelly's men, while a second cave hid the horses.

Outlaw cave, Big Muddy Badlands.
Karpan Photo

Question

A cemetery in this community has a headstone indicating that three people buried here were murdered by RCMP:

a) Moose Jaw
b) Regina
c) Bienfait
d) Alameda
e) Estevan

Answer

c) Bienfait. During the event which became known as the Estevan Riot on September 29, 1931, three striking coal miners were killed in a violent confrontation with the RCMP in downtown Estevan. More than 20 strikers were injured along with several police officers. Miners were seeking better living and working conditions, and higher wages from the coal companies, but were parading illegally.

The bodies of the three miners were buried side-by-side in the Bienfait cemetery, 11 km east of Estevan, their headstone reading "Murdered in Estevan September 29, 1931 by RCMP". Sentiment over the event and the controversial headstone remained high for many years, with the word "murdered" having been both obliterated and painted over again.

Karpan Photo

25

Question

In which Saskatchewan museum can you see Sergeant Bill, a goat that served overseas in World War I and has the medals to prove it?

a) Broderick
b) Broadview
c) Bengough
d) Blaine Lake
e) Borden

Answer

b) Sergeant Bill is in the Broadview Museum, wearing the medals he received including the 1914 Star, the General Service Medal, and the Victory Medal.

This remarkable military career began in 1914 when a girl from Broadview presented her pet goat to the 5th Canadian Infantry Battalion as a mascot. Sergeant Bill became a favorite among the men, although they said he had a tendency to "butt in".

Bill went into the trenches near Armentiers, was gassed during the Second Battle of Ypres, was wounded by shrapnel at Festhubert, and suffered from trench feet. When he disappeared one day, the men worried that he may have been captured by the Bengal Lancers from India who had a fondness for goat meat.

But Bill survived World War I and returned to Saskatchewan. When he died, Bill was stuffed, mounted, and placed in the Saskatchewan Legislative Building. Eventually he was returned to Broadview where he now has a place of honor in the Broadview Museum.

Sergeant Bill and a trooper.   Saskatchewan Archives R-A 10210 (1)

Question

Approximately how many items are in the full collection of Saskatchewan's four branches of the Western Development Museum?

a) 15,000
b) 25,000
c) 50,000
d) 70,000
e) 95,000

Answer

d) 70,000. The Western Development Museum operates four branches – Saskatoon, North Battleford, Moose Jaw, and Yorkton. Of the more than 70,000 artifacts in the total collection, the branches are able to display about 34,000.

Question ✓

Which Saskatchewan community was the site of the largest Ku Klux Klan gathering ever held in Canada?

a) Moose Jaw
b) Regina
c) Swift Current
d) Yorkton
e) Estevan

Answer

a) On June 7, 1927, over 7,000 people attended the Ku Klux Klan rally in Moose Jaw. During its short history in Canada, the Klan had a major following in Saskatchewan, with membership in the tens of thousands. They professed Protestantism, high moral standards, and the purity of the white race, while blaming almost everything on immigrants, French Canadians and Roman Catholics. They burned crosses in communities such as Moose Jaw and Regina. The Klan's

support was a factor in the election of the Conservatives in the 1929 provincial election. One reason for the Klan's following in Moose Jaw was that residents were looking for ways to clean up bootlegging, rum-running and other illicit activities. Saskatchewan soon grew weary of the white-hooded demagogues, and in the early 1930s the KKK faded almost as quickly as it had appeared.

Burning Cross in Regina, 1928.
Saskatchewan Archives R-A 16411

Question

Where was the Red Cross flag first used in Canada?

a) At a dedication ceremony in Regina in 1890
b) During the Mounted Police march west in 1874
c) During the Northwest Rebellion in 1885
d) When Saskatchewan became a province in 1905
e) During the aftermath of the Regina Tornado of 1912

Answer

c) The now-familiar Red Cross insignia was first used in
Canada during the Northwest Rebellion of 1885 at the battles
of Fish Creek and Batoche. Surgeon-Major George Sterling
Ryerson, who travelled with the Canadian militia under
General Middleton, placed the sign of the Red Cross on his
horse-drawn ambulance, hoping that the insignia would
protect him from being attacked.

Canada's first Red Cross flag.   Karpan Photo

Question

Which community in southern Saskatchewan was nicknamed "Little Chicago" for its shady characters and bootlegging activities during the Roaring Twenties?

a) Shaunavon
b) Moose Jaw
c) Estevan
d) Assiniboia
e) Maple Creek

Answer

b) It was the illicit activities centred primarily around River Street that earned Moose Jaw its nickname of "Little Chicago". During Prohibition, Moose Jaw became a centre for smuggling booze. It is even rumored that American gangster Al Capone visited Moose Jaw during these heady times.

Beneath the streets of downtown Moose Jaw, an elaborate system of tunnels, possibly built by Chinese railway workers, connected several buildings during the late 1800s. It is said that the tunnels later served not only as a place to store the booze, but were also used as hideaways, and venues for gambling, prostitution, and opium dens.

Question

Which Saskatchewan city was named after someone who died when the *Titanic* sank in 1912?

Answer

Melville was named after Charles Melville Hays, who was President of the Grand Trunk Railway. He was a passenger on the *Titanic*.

Question ✓

This incident was a major catalyst in the formation of the North West Mounted Police in 1873:

a) Cypress Hills Massacre
b) Frog Lake Massacre
c) Seven Oaks Massacre
d) Louis Riel's return to Canada from the USA
e) The arrival in Canada of Chief Sitting Bull and 5,000 Sioux

Answer

a) Cypress Hills Massacre. In 1873, Parliament passed a bill to establish the North West Mounted Police. However, Prime Minister John A. Macdonald saw no hurry to establish the force; he thought that the following year would be soon enough.

News of the Cypress Hills Massacre changed all that. In May, 1873 in the Cypress Hills, a group of American wolf hunters from Fort Benton, Montana massacred several Assiniboine Indians in retaliation for stealing horses. This event led to heightened concerns about lawlessness in the Northwest, prompting Macdonald to move quickly to appoint the first officers and begin recruitment for the force.

Question ✓

What year did the railway arrive in what is now Saskatchewan?

Answer

In 1882, the Canadian Pacific Railway was extended from Manitoba into what is now Saskatchewan.

Question ✓

Which group of immigrant settlers has the motto "Toil and Peaceful Life"?

a) Mennonites
b) Hutterites
c) Doukhobors
d) Quakers
e) Barr Colonists

Answer

c) Doukhobors are a pacifist sect whose roots go back to the late 1700s in Russia. Persecuted for their beliefs, especially for their stand against violence and serving in the military, more than 7,000 Doukhobors came to Canada in 1899 seeking refuge. A major settlement was Veregin, which is west of Kamsack, named after Doukhobor leader Peter Verigin.

Question ✓

Name the famous novelist who assisted the Doukhobors to migrate to Canada.

Answer

Russian novelist Leo Tolstoy had heard of the Doukhobors' plight and contributed proceeds from his novel *Resurrection* to aid in financing their move.

Question

Name the Finnish immigrant who built a ship in Saskatchewan, intending to sail back to Finland.

Answer

Tom Sukanen homesteaded near Macrorie, and became obsessed with returning to his native Finland in a ship he had built himself. A skilled blacksmith and mechanic, Sukanen crafted most of the parts for his 10-metre (33-foot) boat during the 1930s. He also hand-built many of his own tools, instruments, and a steam motor to propel the ship.

Sukanen transported the ship part way to the South Saskatchewan River, but his dream was never realized. His failing health and obsessive behavior prompted concerned neighbors to move him to the Battleford Hospital where he died in 1943. His ship, the *Dontianen*, is displayed at the Sukanen Ship, Pioneer Village & Museum, 13 km south of Moose Jaw.

Sukanen's ship.   Karpan Photo

Question

How tall was Edouard Beaupré, also known as the Willow Bunch Giant?

a) 2.26 metres (7 feet 5 inches)
b) 2.36 metres (7 feet 9 inches)
c) 2.44 metres (8 feet)
d) 2.51 metres (8 feet 3 inches)
e) 2.59 metres (8 feet 6 inches)

Answer

d) Edouard Beaupré grew to an astounding height of 2.51 metres (8 feet 3 inches). Although he was a normal size when he was born in 1881, his growth spurted as he got older. He was known as being mild-mannered and shy, but didn't enjoy being teased about his height. If children poked fun at him, it is said he would lift them up and leave them on a roof of a house until they had learned their lesson.

He longed to be a cowboy, but his long legs dragged on the ground when he rode a horse, and his weight of almost 181 kg (400 pounds) was too much for a horse to bear.

Beaupré went on tour and appeared in circus-type shows where he would demonstrate his Herculean strength in feats such as lifting up a horse. He contracted tuberculosis and died in St. Louis, Missouri in 1904 at the age of 23. His body was embalmed, then exhibited in shows, and studied at the University of Montreal. In 1990, his cremated remains were finally laid to rest in Willow Bunch, after many years of legal wrangling as to who had rights to the body.

The Willow Bunch Museum has a life-size replica of the Giant who had a 61 cm (24 inch) neck, 147 cm (58 inch) chest, 132 cm (52 inch) waist, and wore size 22 shoes. Displays pertaining to the Giant include his 2.75 metre (9 foot) bed.

*Edouard Beaupré,
the Willow Bunch Giant.*

Saskatchewan Archives R-A 3465

Question ✓

A major street in this community was built along one of the longest straight surveyed lines in North America:

a) Creighton
b) Regina
c) Pierceland
d) Lloydminster
e) Macklin

Answer

d) Lloydminster's 50th Avenue is built along the Fourth Meridian, a straight line that runs along the entire border between Saskatchewan and Alberta.

Question

The original name for the place that eventually became Regina was a Cree word "oskana" which later became "Wascana". What does the Cree word mean?

a) Treeless prairie
b) Place of many mosquitoes
c) Place of abundant goose droppings
d) Bones
e) Creek of bad tasting water

Answer

d) The word "oskana" means "bones" and referred to buffalo bones piled near a pound where the Cree processed buffalo meat. The site had access to water in a creek, and level banks beside the creek for drying hides. As the mound grew over the years, the place became known as "pile of bones". The story goes that after Captain Palliser heard the name of the place, he recorded it as "Wascana", and the same name has been used ever since. The pile of bones near the little creek disappeared when Métis settlers sold the bones for fertilizer.

Settlers started arriving in the early 1880s and set up camp on the fertile plains near Wascana Creek. More settlers moved in when it was learned that a railway station would be built near the spot where the railway line crossed the creek.

The settlement was then chosen as the new capital of the North-West Territories, although criticism ran high. A comment in the *Manitoba Free Press* portrayed the new site as "in the midst of a vast plain of inferior soil...with about enough water in the miserable creek known as Pile 'o Bones to wash a sheep..."

Working the Land

Question ✓

What percentage of Canada's total agricultural land (cultivated and pasture) is found in Saskatchewan?

Answer

39%. According to the 2001 Census of Agriculture, Canada had 67.5 million ha (166.8 million acres) in agricultural land. Saskatchewan had 26.3 million ha (64.9 million acres) in agricultural land, which works out to about 39%.

Question ✓

Approximately what percentage of Saskatchewan's total area consists of farm land?

a) 20%
b) 30%
c) 40%
d) 50%
e) 60%

Answer

c) According to the 2001 Census of Agriculture, Saskatchewan farm land covered about 263,000 sq km, which is just over 40% of Saskatchewan's total area of 652,330 sq km. This is the largest area of farm land of any province in Canada. Alberta is in second place with farms covering 211,000 sq km.

Question ✓

The number of grain elevators in Saskatchewan reached a peak during the 1932-33 crop year. How many were there?

a) 1,282
b) 1,634
c) 2,820
d) 3,240
e) 3,859

Answer

d) According to the Canadian Grain Commission's publication *Grain Elevators in Canada*, Saskatchewan elevator numbers reached a peak of 3,240 in 1932-33.

———•◆━●━◆•———

Question

The number of grain elevators operated by the Saskatchewan Wheat Pool reached a peak in 1972. How many Pool elevators were there?

a) 1,014
b) 1,216
c) 1,626
d) 1,894
e) 1,987

Answer

c) In 1972, the Saskatchewan Wheat Pool operated 1,626 elevators in Saskatchewan.

Question

As of December, 2002 how many primary grain elevators were there in Saskatchewan?

a) 216
b) 482
c) 618
d) 839
e) 950

Answer

a) According to the Canadian Grains Commission, there were 216 primary grain elevators in Saskatchewan, as of December 12, 2002.

Question

Where was the first Saskatchewan Wheat Pool elevator built?

a) Strasbourg
b) Bulyea
c) Wolseley
d) Indian Head
e) Gull Lake

Answer

b) Saskatchewan Wheat Pool elevator #1 was opened on July 1, 1925 at Bulyea.

Question

Where is the oldest surviving grain elevator in Saskatchewan?

Answer

An elevator in Fleming, near the Manitoba border, dates to 1895. It was constructed for the Lake of the Woods Milling Company and had a capacity of 32,000 bushels. Over the years it has been operated by the Saskatchewan Wheat Pool, the United Grain Growers, and has been used for bulk fertilizer storage.

Question

Approximately how many trees and shrubs does the Prairie Farm Rehabilitation Administration (PFRA) Shelterbelt Centre at Indian Head produce and distribute each year?

a) 1 million
b) 3 million
c) 5 million
d) 7 million
e) 8 million

Answer

c) Over 5 million. Located just south of Indian Head on 256 ha (640 acres) of land, the Shelterbelt Centre has a long history going back to 1902 when the original nursery was established to produce hardy trees and shrubs adapted to prairie conditions. Today, 29 species are supplied to farms to assist in curtailing erosion. The trees also provide habitat for birds and animals, and provide shade for farm houses and buildings.

Question

Name the largest livestock show in Canada, based on gross sales.

Answer

Canadian Western Agribition has the highest gross sales of any livestock show in Canada, approximately $3.5 million in each of the last few years. Held each November in Regina's Exhibition Park, Agribition draws visitors from as many as 52 countries around the world. The exhibition showcases prime livestock including sheep, cattle, horses, elk, goats, alpacas, llamas and bison. A rodeo, dances and many other events round out this major agricultural show.

Purebred Beef Show.   Canadian Western Agribition Photo

Question

Which barn was considered the largest barn in North America at the time it was built?

a) Smith Barn near Leader
b) Bell Barn near Indian Head
c) Robertson Barn at Zealandia
d) Motherwell Homestead barn near Abernethy
e) Main Barn at the University of Saskatchewan

Answer

a) Smith Barn. William T. "Horseshoe" Smith, originally from Kentucky, farmed on a grand scale in the Leader district. He pastured large numbers of livestock, with 2,000 horses, 2,000 hogs, 10,000 sheep, and 1,600 mules.

In 1914, Smith began building an enormous barn that measured 122 metres (400 feet) long, 39 metres (128 feet) wide, and 18 metres (60 feet) high. A crew of 100 men worked for five months on the project. On the night of its grand opening, two bands were hired – one to play at each end!

Just four years after it was completed, Smith died. A few years later, this monument to excess was torn down, and 875,000 board feet of fir lumber were salvaged.

Today only the foundation remains and a scale model that gives an idea of the incredible size of the barn. To visit the barn site, head west of Leader on grid road #741 and follow the signs.

Model of the Smith Barn.   Karpan Photo

Question ✓

How many dozen eggs does Saskatchewan produce each year?

a) 500,000 dozen
b) 2,000,000 dozen
c) 8,000,000 dozen
d) 12,000,000 dozen
e) 22,000,000 dozen

Answer

e) According to Statistics Canada figures, Saskatchewan egg production in recent years has been around 22,000,000 dozen or 264,000,000 eggs. The 1 million hens laying those eggs were sure kept busy, averaging about 264 eggs per hen per year!

Question ✓

Saskatchewan has about 1,300 beekeepers with some 100,000 bee colonies. Approximately how many kilograms of honey were produced in 2001?

a) 3 million kilograms
b) 4 million kilograms
c) 6 million kilograms
d) 8 million kilograms
e) 10 million kilograms

Answer

e) According to Saskatchewan Agriculture, 9.75 million kilograms of honey were produced in 2001. It sounds even more impressive when you look at the imperial measurements – 21.5 million pounds! In 2001, Saskatchewan also jumped to first place as the largest honey producer in Canada. As well, Saskatchewan takes the cake for the highest per colony yield of honey of any province, at approximately 109 kg or 240 pounds.

Question

How many farms are there in Saskatchewan?

Answer

According to the 2001 Census of Agriculture, Saskatchewan had 50,598 farms. This was down from 56,979 farms in 1996, and 60,840 farms in 1991. The highest number of farms reported in Saskatchewan was 142,391 in the 1936 census.

The Wheat Province?

Question ✓

Based on the 2001 Census of Agriculture, Saskatchewan accounted for half or more of Canada's total production of these crops:

a) spring wheat
b) durum
c) barley
d) flax
e) mustard
f) canola
g) lentils
h) field peas
i) canary seed

Answer

a, b, d, e, f, g, h, i) Saskatchewan's share of the 2001 Canadian crop was: spring wheat – 57%, durum – 81%, flax – 70%, canola – 50%, mustard – 82%, lentils – 98%, field peas – 77%, canary seed – 86%.

In 2001, Saskatchewan produced about 40% of Canada's barley crop.

Question

Saskatchewan accounts for almost three-quarters of total world production of this crop:

a) mustard
b) field peas
c) lentils
d) canary seed
e) flax

Answer

d) When it comes to canary seed, Saskatchewan is definitely where the action is. Saskatchewan Agriculture indicates that the province averaged about 155,000 tonnes per year between 1992 and 2001, which is roughly 75% of world production. Canary seed is used as feed for wild and captive birds. Almost half of the exports go to Europe, and the rest all over the globe. One of the largest customers is Mexico.

Any of the above choices would have been good guesses. In recent years, Saskatchewan also produced 49% of the world's mustard, 23% of its lentils, 14% of its field peas, and 27% of its flax.

Question ✓

How many cattle are there in Saskatchewan?

Answer

According to the 2001 Census of Agriculture, there were 2.9 million cattle on Saskatchewan farms.

Question

Saskatchewan farmers plant more wheat than any other crop. What is the second most popular crop in terms of acres planted, based on the average from 1992-2001?

a) barley
b) oats
c) durum
d) canola
e) flax
f) peas
g) lentils

Answer

d) Saskatchewan's second largest crop is canola, a crop that did not even exist 30 years ago. According to Statistics Canada, the average during 1992-2001 was 5.4 million seeded acres (2.18 million ha), second only to wheat with an average of 12.4 million seeded acres (5 million ha).

Canola in bloom.   Karpan Photo

Question ✓

Saskatchewan is the world's largest exporter of these crops:

a) wheat
b) barley
c) mustard
d) lentils
e) canary seed

Answer

c, d, e) Mustard, lentils and canary seed. In recent years, no other jurisdiction in the world had a larger share of world exports for any of these three crops.

While Saskatchewan has long been famous for wheat, the province accounts for only 2-3% of wheat grown in the world.

Question ✓

On average, how many kilograms of processed wild rice are produced in Saskatchewan each year?

Answer

The ten-year average production figure during the 1990s was 567,000 kg (1.25 million pounds) of processed wild rice. In 1998 and 1999, production vastly exceeded the average, yielding an amazing 794,000 kg (1.75 million pounds) and 1,020,500 kg (2.25 million pounds) respectively. Yields are generally higher in years when water levels are low, since shallow water is better suited to growing wild rice.

Question ✓

What percentage of Canada's wild rice crop was produced in Saskatchewan, based on the average from 1997-2001?

a) 40%
b) 50%
c) 60%
d) 70%
e) 80%

Answer

d) According to Saskatchewan Agriculture statistics, Saskatchewan accounted for 70% of all the wild rice grown in Canada during this time. Saskatchewan's production was exceptionally high in 1998 and 1999, when it accounted for 80% of Canada's production. About 250 producers are involved in growing wild rice in the northern part of the province. Most of the production is exported to the United States.

Harvesting wild rice.   Saskatchewan Agriculture Photo

Furthermore, If I Get Elected...

Question

Who was the first premier of Saskatchewan?

a) Edgar Dewdney
b) Walter Scott
c) Charles Dunning
d) Amédée Forget
e) James Gardiner

Answer

b) When Saskatchewan became a province in September, 1905, Lieutenant Governor Amédée Forget appointed Walter Scott as premier. Scott was to hold office until the first provincial election was called.

Scott had a background in journalism and printing. He was elected a Liberal Member of Parliament in 1900, but resigned in 1905 to focus his attention on the provincial scene. In August, 1905, he became leader of the provincial Liberal party, then formed the first government of Saskatchewan when he was named premier. Scott called the first provincial election for December 13, 1905, which he won. He later led the Liberals to victory in the elections of 1908 and 1912. Under his administration, roads and bridges were built to deal with the increasing number of settlers, women were given the vote, co-operatives were formed, railway lines were expanded, and better health and education facilities were established.

Following a period of illness, Walter Scott resigned from public office in 1916. He died in 1938.

Walter Scott, first premier of Saskatchewan.

Saskatchewan Archives S-B 3710

Question

Which of the following politicians were born in Saskatchewan?

a) Tommy Douglas
b) John Diefenbaker
c) Allan Blakeney
d) Grant Devine
e) Roy Romanow
f) Ross Thatcher

Answer

d, e, f) Grant Devine, Roy Romanow, and Ross Thatcher. Grant Devine was born in 1944 in Regina, Roy Romanow was born in 1939 in Saskatoon, and Ross Thatcher was born in 1917 in Neville, Saskatchewan.

Tommy Douglas was born in 1904 in Falkirk, Scotland. John Diefenbaker was born in 1895 in Neustadt, Ontario. Allan Blakeney was born in 1925 in Bridgewater, Nova Scotia.

Question

For many years the CCF party, which later became the New Democratic Party, formed the government in Saskatchewan. What does the acronym "CCF" stand for?

a) Christian Co-operative Federation
b) Co-operative Commonwealth Federation
c) Canadian Capitalist Federation
d) Canadian Commonwealth Federation
e) Canadian Co-operative Federation

Answer

b) The Co-operative Commonwealth Federation was formed in 1933, primarily by socialists, farmers and labor representatives. The first leader of this new left-leaning political party was J.S. Woodsworth, a Member of Parliament. While a national party, the CCF's main stronghold was Saskatchewan where it formed the government in 1944, led by T.C. "Tommy" Douglas.

In 1961, a founding convention was held to discuss the merger of the national CCF party and organized labor. The name "New Democratic Party" was decided upon, with Tommy Douglas elected the first leader of the new national party.

Question

Who was the longest-serving premier of Saskatchewan?

a) Jimmy Gardiner
b) Woodrow Lloyd
c) Ross Thatcher
d) Tommy Douglas
e) Roy Romanow

Answer

d) Tommy Douglas was premier from 1944 to 1961.

T.C. "Tommy" Douglas. Saskatchewan Archives R-A 10679-3

Question

In which community did Tommy Douglas serve as a Baptist minister before he became premier of Saskatchewan?

a) Wakaw
b) Weyburn
c) Whitewood
d) Wynyard
e) Wapella

Answer

b) Tommy Douglas' first parish was Calvary Baptist Church in Weyburn. Originally located downtown, the church is now on 10th Avenue on Signal Hill where it houses a performing arts centre, along with a small area devoted to Douglas memorabilia.

Calvary Church, Weyburn.   Karpan Photo

Question

How many times was John Diefenbaker elected a Member of Parliament?

a) 5
b) 7
c) 10
d) 13
e) 15

Answer

d) John Diefenbaker was elected to Parliament 13 times between 1940 and 1979. He tried for a federal seat as early as 1925, but was unsuccessful. Highlights of his career included the Progressive Conservative upset victory in 1957, when he became prime minister. The following year, Diefenbaker led the Conservatives to victory again with 208 seats, which at that time was the highest number of seats ever won by a political party. Diefenbaker died in office in 1979, only a few months after his thirteenth parliamentary win.

John Diefenbaker.

Diefenbaker Canada Centre

Question

Where is the only Prime Ministerial Centre in Canada?

Answer

The Diefenbaker Canada Centre in Saskatoon is the only facility in Canada based on the official papers and collections of a former prime minister. The official papers of all former prime ministers are housed in the Public Archives of Canada, with two exceptions – the R.B. Bennett papers, which are in the University of New Brunswick Library, and the J.G. Diefenbaker papers, which are in Saskatoon.

The Diefenbaker Canada Centre on the grounds of the University of Saskatchewan is a combination working archives and museum featuring Canadian history, the development of western Canada, and numerous travelling exhibits. Among the highlights are the replicas of the Prime Minister's East Block Office, and the Privy Council Chamber, both decorated to the 1957-1963 era when Diefenbaker served as Canada's thirteenth prime minister.

Privy Council Chamber replica.　　　　　　　　　　Karpan Photo

Question ✓

Who was the first woman in Saskatchewan to be elected a Member of the Legislative Assembly?

Answer

Sarah Ramsland was married to Magnus O. Ramsland, Liberal MLA for the Pelly constituency. Following Mr. Ramsland's sudden death during the 1918 flu epidemic, Sarah decided to try to continue her husband's work by running in the 1919 by-election. She won and became Saskatchewan's first woman MLA. She went on to win the 1921 general election, but was defeated in 1925.

She is remembered for her efforts in urging the province to mark its historic sites. On a more mundane matter, the Honourable Member for Pelly once went to see Highways Minister Gardiner about getting a small road problem fixed. Gardiner put her off, so she reportedly sat down, took her crocheting out of her bag, and told him she was prepared to wait as long as necessary. Gardiner then relented.

Sarah Ramsland, Saskatchewan's first woman MLA.

Saskatchewan Archives S-B 9404

Question

Name the first woman in Canada to be appointed Minister of Finance.

Answer

In January, 1993, Janice MacKinnon was appointed Minister of Finance of Saskatchewan, becoming the first woman in Canada to hold that portfolio. She held the position until June, 1997.

Question

Who was the first woman to lead a political party in Saskatchewan?

Answer

In 1989, Lynda Haverstock was elected Liberal leader, the first woman in Saskatchewan to lead a political party. She remained leader until 1996 when she stepped down to sit as an independent Member of the Legislative Assembly.

Lynda Haverstock was appointed lieutenant governor in 1999 and installed in 2000, the second woman to serve in this role since Saskatchewan became a province in 1905.

Question ✓

These people all served as Governor General of Canada.
Which were born in Saskatchewan?

a) Roland Michener
b) Vincent Massey
c) Jeanne Sauvé
d) Jules Léger
e) Ray Hnatyshyn

Answer

c, e) Jeanne Sauvé and Ray Hnatyshyn. Jeanne Benoit was
born in Prud'homme on April 26, 1922. She married Maurice
Sauvé in 1948, then launched her career as a journalist and
broadcaster. In 1972, she entered politics and served as a
Liberal Member of Parliament for Montreal. Mme Sauvé
became the first female Speaker of the House in 1980. Four
years later she became the first female governor general of
Canada. She died in 1990.

Ray (Ramon) Hnatyshyn was born in Saskatoon in 1934. For
many years he practised law in Saskatoon, then was elected a
Progressive Conservative Member of Parliament in 1974. In
1990, he was appointed governor general, serving until 1995.
He died in 2002.

Question

Which Saskatchewan community has a statue of former
Governor General Ray Hnatyshyn?

Answer

Saskatoon. The statue is on Spadina Crescent near 24th Street.

Question

Who served the fewest number of years as premier of Saskatchewan?

a) Charles Dunning
b) James Gardiner
c) William Martin
d) James Anderson
e) Woodrow Lloyd

Answer

e) Woodrow Lloyd of the CCF/NDP was premier from November, 1961 to May, 1964.

Question ✓

Who was Saskatchewan's first lieutenant governor?

a) Edgar Dewdney
b) Walter Scott
c) Amédée Forget
d) Joseph Royal
e) James Walsh

Answer

c) Amédée Forget held office from 1898-1910. He served as the last lieutenant governor of the North-West Territories (1898-1905), and was reappointed the first lieutenant governor of the province of Saskatchewan (1905-1910).

Question

Which lieutenant governor had a pet monkey?

a) Edgar Dewdney
b) Amédée Forget
c) David Laird
d) Malcolm Cameron
e) George Porteous

Answer

b) Lieutenant Governor Amédée Forget had a pet spider monkey named Jocko.

Amédée Forget and his pet monkey Jocko.
Saskatchewan Archives R-A 7593

Question

What toy did Lieutenant Governor Forget have in his study for his pet monkey to play on?

a) teeter-totter
b) rocking horse
c) monkey bars
d) swing
e) skateboard

Answer

b) Jocko played on a rocking horse, although it seems he preferred swinging from the light fixtures and cords rather than playing with his toys. In an attempt to curb this behavior, ropes were installed in the spacious skylight well at Government House for Jocko to swing from, but the story goes that he still favored the light fixtures. Government House in Regina is restored to the period when the Forgets lived there, complete with Jocko's rocking horse in the study.

Jocko's rocking horse, Government House, Regina.   Karpan Photo

Question ✓

Which member of a Canadian champion curling team became lieutenant governor of Saskatchewan?

Answer

Sylvia Fedoruk was a member of the Joyce McKee rink that won the Canadian Women's Championship in 1961. She was also on the Joyce McKee rink that won the Provincial Women's Championship in 1960, 1961 and 1962. Fedoruk served as Saskatchewan's lieutenant governor from 1988 to 1994, the first woman in Saskatchewan to serve in this position.

Sylvia Fedoruk excelled in track and field, golf, volleyball, and basketball during her student years at the University of Saskatchewan.

On the academic side, she was a member of the University of Saskatchewan research team that developed Cobalt 60 units for cancer treatment. She was named an Officer of the Order of Canada, served as Chancellor of the University, and has received several honorary doctorate degrees.

Doing Business

Question ✓

Name the largest scientific project in Canada since the 1960s.

Answer

Canada's largest scientific project is the Canadian Light Source at the University of Saskatchewan. It is the largest project since the 1960s, both in terms of dollar value, and the size and importance of the facility. It houses a synchrotron that produces brilliant light – millions of times more brilliant than the sun – that allows scientists to examine biological, geological, and chemical samples with higher accuracy and precision than has previously been possible in Canada.

The synchrotron has many uses in research, such as developing new drugs, designing new high-power computer microchips, developing stronger metal alloys, analyzing ore samples from mines, and identifying chemical contaminants, to name a few.

The $173.5 million project has been endorsed by 18 universities besides the University of Saskatchewan. This is the first scientific project in Canada to involve a partnership between a university and federal, provincial, and civic authorities. As the only synchrotron in Canada, this national facility assists Canadian researchers who would otherwise have to use facilities in other countries.

Question ✓

Saskatchewan is the largest producer and exporter of uranium in the world.

a) True
b) False

Answer

a) True. Saskatchewan produces approximately 32% of the uranium in the world, and accounts for 100% of the uranium produced in Canada. Saskatchewan is also the world's largest exporter of the mineral which is used to fuel nuclear power plants around the world.

The rich uranium deposits in Saskatchewan are concentrated in the Athabasca basin. Ore is extracted from open pit and underground mines, then milled to separate the uranium. At current production levels, uranium reserves will last about another 30 years.

Cameco Corporation, the largest uranium producer in the world, operates several mines in Saskatchewan. The McArthur River mine in north central Saskatchewan is the largest high-grade uranium mine in the world, and nearby Key Lake is the world's largest high-grade uranium milling operation.

Question ✓

Saskatchewan generates most of its electricity from:

a) hydro
b) coal
c) nuclear
d) natural gas
e) wind

Answer

b) Approximately 75% of the electricity generated in Saskatchewan comes from coal-fired power stations. About 10 million tonnes of coal are mined each year, with almost 90% used in power stations.

Question

How much coal is required to produce enough electricity to power a 100-watt light bulb for eight hours?

a) .5 kg
b) 1 kg
c) 1.5 kg
d) 3 kg
e) 5 kg

Answer

a) .5 kg or about one pound of coal.

Question ✓

Name the largest lignite coal-burning thermal power station in Canada.

a) Poplar River power station near Coronach
b) Boundary Dam power station near Estevan
c) Queen Elizabeth power station in Saskatoon
d) Shand power station near Estevan
e) Coteau Creek power station near Lake Diefenbaker

Answer

b) Boundary Dam power station, just south of Estevan, is both the largest thermal generating power station in Saskatchewan, and the largest lignite coal-burning station in Canada. It is capable of producing 875 megawatts of electricity from six turbine generators, about half of the electricity generated in the province. Poplar River power station near Coronach is the second largest station at 592 megawatts, while Shand ranks third at 300 megawatts. Coal is not used at either the Queen Elizabeth or Coteau Creek power stations.

Boundary Dam power station.

Karpan Photo

Question ✓

Where was the first co-operative established in Saskatchewan?

a) Battleford
b) Meadow Lake
c) Hamona
d) Midale
e) Coronach

Answer

c) Hamona. The Harmony Industrial Association was formed in 1895 in Beulah, Manitoba with a view to establishing a new order of society where co-operation would replace competition. Members found the perfect place to build – in the Qu'Appelle Valley just east of present-day Tantallon, Saskatchewan. Here was good water, plenty of timber, stones for building, and the promise that a railway would pass through.

By 1898, all the members from Manitoba had moved to the valley and Hamona was named. About 50 people lived here, with homes grouped into a village. Besides farming, there were hopes for factories, mills and stores.

But the dream was short-lived. By 1900, the colony had disbanded because of disagreements over communal living and disappointment that the railway hadn't come. However, the co-operative ideal didn't die with the colony; some of Hamona's residents played a role in later Saskatchewan co-operative movements.

Today there are more than 1,400 co-operatives operating throughout Saskatchewan in areas that include agriculture, resources, community development, education, health care, recreation, and financial services.

Question ✓

The first automated teller machine (ATM) in Canada was introduced in Saskatchewan by this financial institution:

a) Bank of Montreal
b) Saskatchewan Credit Union
c) Canadian Imperial Bank of Commerce
d) Royal Bank
e) Bank of Nova Scotia

Answer

b) The Saskatchewan Credit Union introduced the first ATM machine in Canada at Regina's Sherwood Credit Union in 1976.

Question ✓

The first in-store direct debit system in Canada was piloted in Saskatchewan by this financial institution:

a) Bank of Montreal
b) Saskatchewan Credit Union
c) Canadian Imperial Bank of Commerce
d) Royal Bank
e) Bank of Nova Scotia

Answer

b) The Saskatchewan Credit Union was the first, in 1986.

Question

The potash mine near this Saskatchewan community is the largest in the world:

a) Esterhazy
b) Allan
c) Belle Plaine
d) Vanscoy
e) Lanigan

Answer

a) This distinction belongs to the International Minerals and Chemicals (IMC) mine near Esterhazy. Their first mine, K-1, was begun in 1957 and has been producing continuously since 1962. Five years later the company opened K-2 mine 10 km away. The mines are connected underground and have a combined capacity of 3.81 million tonnes of finished product annually.

Drilling is done approximately 945 metres (3,100 feet) underground using machines known as Marietta Miners. It takes about three minutes for these electrically powered behemoths to advance one metre through the potash ore, cutting a swath about four metres wide and 2.5 metres high. The raw ore is moved to the back of the machine where it is fed onto a conveyor belt which transports it to the shaft. Then it is transported to the surface for processing to separate the salt from the potash.

IMC Potash K-2 Mine.   IMC Potash Photo

Question

Saskatchewan Minerals is the largest producer in Canada and the United States of this mineral:

a) potash
b) nickel
c) gold
d) copper
e) sodium sulphate

Answer

e) Saskatchewan Minerals produces sodium sulphate at its facilities near Chaplin Lake and Ingebrigt Lake. The company is the largest natural sodium sulphate producer in Canada and the United States. Sodium sulphate is used in many common household products including dishwasher and powder laundry detergent, carpet deodorizers, modified corn starch, paper, and glass.

Sweeeeep!!

Question ✓

Where is the first and only major museum in the world dedicated to curling?

a) Regina
b) Prince Albert
c) Estevan
d) Weyburn
e) North Battleford

Answer

d) Weyburn's Turner Curling Museum is not only the first of its kind in the world, but it also has the largest collection of curling memorabilia anywhere in the world. Started by Don and Elva Turner, the museum displays hundreds of brooms, rocks, photographs, books, crests, sweaters, and practically any other curling-related item you can image. The collection of curling pins alone numbers over 18,000. Among the most unusual items are curling irons dating to around 1760 made from melted cannonballs.

Don Turner, Turner Curling Museum.

Karpan Photo

Question ✓

Where was the first recorded curling game played in what is now Saskatchewan?

a) Regina
b) Saskatoon
c) Prince Albert
d) Batoche
e) Cumberland House

Answer

c) The first recorded game was played on the North Saskatchewan River in Prince Albert on January 17, 1882. For "rocks" the players used blocks of wood cut from tamarack trees.

Question ✓

In the early 1900s, the sport of curling spread across Saskatchewan like a prairie fire. Which communities claimed to have the world's largest curling rink?

a) Prince Albert
b) Regina
c) Saskatoon
d) Swift Current
e) Moose Jaw

Answer

b, c, e) Regina, Saskatoon, Moose Jaw. In 1909, the Regina Curling Club built the world's largest curling rink with 9 sheets of ice. The following year, Moose Jaw built a 10-sheet rink, giving it the record. Then in 1912, an 11-sheet rink was built in Saskatoon. At that time, Saskatchewan had the three biggest curling rinks in the world.

———— ·•·◆·•·— ————

Question

Who was skip of the Saskatchewan women's curling team that won an unprecedented three consecutive Canadian championships?

Answer

It was Vera Pezer's rink of Sheila Rowan, Joyce McKee and Lenore Morrison who captured the Canadian women's curling championship in 1971, 1972, and 1973.

Question

Who was skip of the curling team that won the first Canadian Women's Curling Championship in 1961?

Answer

The Joyce McKee rink of Saskatoon, with Sylvia Fedoruk, Barbara MacNevin, and Rosa McFee, won the championship.

Question

Who was skip of the Saskatchewan men's curling team that won an unprecedented four Briers in five years?

Answer

Skip Ernie Richardson played with his brother Garnet, and cousins Arnold and Wes. They won the Brier, the Canadian men's curling championship, in 1959, 1960, 1962, and 1963.

The Ernie Richardson team with Premier Tommy Douglas.
Saskatchewan Archives R-A 11522

The Olympians

Question ✓

Which Saskatchewan team won the first ever Olympic gold medal in women's curling?

Answer

Sandra Schmirler's team of Jan Betker, Marcia Gudereit, Joan McCusker, and Anita Ford captured the gold at the 1998 Winter Olympics in Nagano, Japan. In the deciding game, they defeated Denmark by a score of 7-5.

In addition to numerous wins at the provincial and national levels, Schmirler skipped her team to victory in the world women's championships in 1993, 1994, and 1997.

Question ✓

Name the Saskatchewan-born athlete who won Canada's first gold medal in women's speedskating.

Answer

Catriona Le May Doan captured the gold in the 500-metre races at the Winter Olympics in Nagano, Japan in 1998. She followed that with another gold at the 2002 Winter Olympics in Salt Lake City.

Question ✓

Name the Saskatchewan athlete who won Canada's only gold medal in the 1952 Olympics, and Canada's first Olympic gold medal since 1936.

Answer

George Genereux was just 17 years old when he won a gold medal for Canada in trap shooting at the 1952 Olympic Games in Helsinki, Finland. This was the first gold medal won by a Canadian athlete since the 1936 Olympics. Genereux's score in clay pigeon trapshooting was 192 out of a possible 200, just one shot better than the silver medal winner from Sweden.

Question ✓

Name the Saskatchewan athlete who won the only gold medal in track and field for Canada in the 1920 Olympics.

Answer

Earl Thomson, born near Birch Hills, won gold for Canada in the 110-metre hurdles at the 1920 Olympics, held in Antwerp, Belgium.

Thomson was also the first man to break the 15-second barrier in the 110-metre hurdles when he set a world record of 14.8 seconds in 1916. He later set a new record of 14.4 seconds, which stood for 11 years.

Question ✓

Who was the only female athlete to win an Olympic gold medal for Canada in an individual track and field event?

Answer

Ethel Catherwood won a gold medal in high jump at the 1928 Olympics in Amsterdam. To date, it remains the only Olympic gold medal for track and field won by a Canadian woman in an individual event.

Catherwood was attending Bedford Road Collegiate in Saskatoon when her high-jumping talents came to the attention of track and field coach Joe Griffiths. At the 1927 provincial track meet in Regina, she easily cleared 1.59 metres (5 feet 2.75 inches), setting a new world record. In 1928, she attended the Olympic games in Amsterdam, the first Olympics where women athletes were allowed to compete. By clearing 1.60 metres (5 feet 3 inches), she won a gold medal in high jump and also set a new world record.

When Ethel Catherwood returned to Saskatoon, rousing celebrations were held for the gold medalist. She became known as the "Saskatoon Lily" for her grace, beauty, and agility.

Beset by injuries, she retired from athletics and moved to the United States, where she died in 1988 after living much of her life in seclusion.

Football Fever

Question

In a playoff game between the Saskatchewan Roughriders and the Calgary Stampeders at Taylor Field in Regina on November 22, 1967, snow and ice made the playing field particularly slippery. Roughrider middle guard Ron Atchison decided to change his footwear from the normal cleats worn by football players. What type of footwear did he put on?

a) running shoes
b) rubber boots
c) hiking boots
d) Hush Puppies
e) Rockports

Answer

d) Atchison chose to wear his Hush Puppies, which he reportedly taped to his feet. As a result, Greb Shoes Ltd. presented him with the "Order of the Bronze Hush Puppies" when they bronzed his left shoe and turned it into a unique trophy. The bronzed shoe is on display at the Saskatchewan Sports Hall of Fame and Museum in Regina. By the way, Saskatchewan won the game.

Question

Taylor Field stadium in Regina is home to the Saskatchewan Roughriders football team. After whom is Taylor Field named?

a) Former Member of Parliament Len Taylor
b) Neil J. "Piffles" Taylor, a Regina alderman
c) Saskatoon bowling champion Marion Taylor
d) Hockey player Fred "Cyclone" Taylor
e) Former Saskatchewan MLA Graham Taylor

Answer

b) Neil "Piffles" Taylor was both an energetic player and supporter of rugby and football in Regina. Taylor is remembered for his agility and ability to figure out the opposition team's strategies.

During World War I, he joined the Royal Flying Corps, was shot down over France and taken prisoner. After the War, he became a lawyer and returned to Regina where he practised law.

Taylor also returned to football, refusing to let the fact that he had lost an eye during the War affect his game. The story goes that Taylor called a halt in play during a game in Calgary in 1919 until he found his glass eye which had popped out during a forceful tackle.

Piffles Taylor later became involved in business and served as a Regina alderman for several years. He was awarded the Order of the British Empire for his participation in World War I. He died in 1947, the same year as Taylor Field was named in his honor.

Question

What type of animal is the Saskatchewan Roughriders' mascot?

a) beaver
b) gopher
c) badger
d) tiger
e) sloth

Answer

b) Gainer the Gopher is the Roughriders' mascot.

Question ✓

Which Grey Cup game involving the Saskatchewan Roughriders produced the highest combined score in Grey Cup history?

a) 1966; Saskatchewan vs. Ottawa
b) 1972; Saskatchewan vs. Hamilton
c) 1976; Saskatchewan vs. Ottawa
d) 1989; Saskatchewan vs. Hamilton
e) 1997; Saskatchewan vs. Toronto

Answer

d) The 1989 Grey Cup game ended with a combined score of 83 when the Saskatchewan Roughriders defeated the Hamilton Tiger-Cats 43-40, winning the Grey Cup for the second time in Saskatchewan's history.

Question

The Saskatchewan Roughriders won the 1989 Grey Cup, defeating the Hamilton Tiger-Cats by a score of 43-40. The game was won when Dave Ridgway kicked the most famous field goal in Grey Cup history in the dying seconds of the last quarter. How many seconds were left?

Answer

With only two seconds remaining in the game, Ridgway's 35-yard field goal was successful at 14:58 of the fourth quarter.

Question

Which Saskatchewan Roughriders player holds the CFL record for passes attempted in one game?

Answer

Kent Austin attempted 65 passes in the September 15, 1991 game between Saskatchewan and Edmonton. Austin also holds the record for the most pass attempts in one season – 770 in 1992.

Question

Which Saskatchewan Roughriders player holds the CFL record for rushing?

Answer

George Reed completed 16,116 yards of rushing during his 13 seasons with the Roughriders, 1963-1975.

Question

Which Saskatchewan Roughriders player holds the CFL record for the longest field goal?

Answer

Paul McCallum kicked a record 62-yard field goal during an October 27, 2001 game against the Edmonton Eskimos. The 62-yarder was one of four field goals McCallum completed that day, leading the Riders to a 12–3 victory. The previous record was held by another Roughrider, Dave Ridgway, who completed a 60-yard field goal in the September 6, 1987 game between Saskatchewan and Winnipeg.

Question

Which Saskatchewan Roughriders player holds the CFL record for most field goals in one season?

Answer

Dave Ridgway scored 59 field goals in 1990.

Question

Which Saskatchewan Roughriders player holds the CFL record for greatest number of touchdowns?

Answer

George Reed scored 137 touchdowns in 13 seasons with the Roughriders from 1963 to 1975.

The Puck Stops Here

Question

Which Saskatchewan-born hockey player holds the NHL record for the most consecutive games by a goal tender?

Answer

Goal tender Glenn Hall, born in Humboldt in 1931, had an 18-year career with the NHL between 1952 and 1971. Of the 906 NHL games he played, 502 were consecutive, the highest number of any goal tender. Hall played four seasons with Detroit, 10 with Chicago, and four with St. Louis. He played 11 times on the NHL All-Star team.

Question

Which Saskatchewan-born hockey player holds the record for the most NHL regular-season games played?

Answer

Gordie Howe, born March 31, 1928 in Floral, Saskatchewan, played 1,767 games in an NHL career that spanned 26 seasons between 1946 and 1980.

Question

Which NHL hockey player from Saskatchewan was known as "The Dipsy Doodle Dandy from Delisle"?

a) Doug Bentley
b) Max Bentley
c) Emile Francis
d) Sid Abel
e) Al Ritchie

Answer

b) Max Bentley was born in Delisle in 1920, and earned this distinctive nickname. Known for his speed and agility, Bentley played 12 NHL seasons between 1940 and 1954. He joined the Chicago Black Hawks, but in 1947 was traded to the Toronto Maple Leafs who gave up five players just to get him. He died in 1984.

Question

Name the Saskatchewan athlete who made history as the first person to play in the Grey Cup and Stanley Cup finals in the same season.

Answer

Regina-born Gerry James played for the Winnipeg Blue Bombers in the 1959 Grey Cup against the Hamilton Tiger-Cats. He also played hockey for the Toronto Maple Leafs in the 1959-60 season when Toronto played the Montreal Canadiens in the Stanley Cup finals.

Question

Which Saskatchewan-born NHL player was a member of the winning team in six Stanley Cups?

a) Glenn Hall
b) Emile Francis
c) Bernie Federko
d) Gordie Howe
e) Bryan Trottier

Answer

e) Bryan Trottier, who was raised in Val Marie, played for the New York Islanders of the NHL when they won four consecutive Stanley Cups from 1980 to 1983. Trottier was a member of the Pittsburgh Penguins when they won the Stanley Cup in 1991 and 1992.

During his 18-year career with the NHL, Trottier accumulated an impressive number of awards including the Calder Memorial trophy for the NHL rookie of the year. In 1979, he won the Hart Trophy for the league's most valuable player, as well as the Art Ross Trophy which recognized Trottier as the leading scorer in the NHL.

World's Greatest Swingers

Question

Saskatchewan has more golfers per capita than anywhere in the world. What percentage of Saskatchewan residents over the age of 12 play six or more rounds of golf per season?

a) 13%
b) 17%
c) 23%
d) 33%
e) 40%

Answer

d) 33%. According to the Saskatchewan Golf Association, this is the highest percentage in the world.

Harbor Golf Course, Elbow.　　　　　　　　　　Karpan Photo

Question

Name the busiest golf course in Saskatchewan.

a) Willows Golf & Country Club, Saskatoon
b) Holiday Park Golf Course, Saskatoon
c) Tor Hill Golf Course, Regina
d) Emerald Park Golf Course, Regina
e) Waskesiu Golf Course
f) North Battleford Golf & Country Club

Answer

b) At Holiday Park Golf Course in Saskatoon, well over 78,000 rounds of golf were played in each of the past few years, the highest in the province. Prior to 1991 when a number of new golf courses came on stream in the Saskatoon area, golfers played as many as 96,000 rounds of golf in a year at Holiday Park. At one point, it was considered the busiest golf course in Canada.

Question

Which Saskatchewan golf course was the first in Canada to be named after a woman?

Answer

Joanne Goulet Golf Course. In 1993, an 18-hole golf course in northwest Regina was named after Joanne Goulet. A resident of Regina, Goulet has an impressive number of wins to her name – 32 women's city championships, 17 provincial championships, and twice a member of the provincial team that won the national championships. She has competed across Canada and the United States, as well as overseas.

Question

Where would you be playing golf if you hit the ball at the 9th tee and the ball landed an hour later in another country?

Answer

North Portal. Gateway Cities Golf Club straddles the Canada/U.S.A. border at Portal, North Dakota and North Portal, Saskatchewan. The first eight holes and the 9th tee are in Saskatchewan, but the 9th hole and club house are in North Dakota. During golf season, North Dakota is on daylight saving time, so if you hit the ball in Saskatchewan at 2 p.m., it would land in North Dakota at 3 p.m.

Question

Where is the most northerly golf course in Saskatchewan?

a) Stony Rapids
b) Meadow Lake
c) La Ronge
d) Waskesiu
e) Candle Lake

Answer

c) The 9-hole course at Eagle Point Resort is just north of La Ronge on McGibbon Bay.

Lay of the Land

Question ✓

How many degrees of latitude are there between Saskatchewan's northern and southern border?

Answer

The northern border of Saskatchewan is the 60th parallel, and its southern border is the 49th. The difference is 11 degrees of latitude.

Question

What part of Saskatchewan has the lowest elevation above sea level?

a) Lake Athabasca
b) Cumberland Delta
c) Qu'Appelle Valley
d) Primrose Lake
e) Big Muddy Valley

Answer

a) At 213 metres (699 feet) above sea level, Lake Athabasca has the lowest elevation in the province.

Question

What part of Saskatchewan has the highest elevation above sea level?

a) Cypress Hills
b) Wood Mountain
c) Vermillion Hills
d) Coteau Hills
e) Duck Mountain

Answer

a) The highest point of land in Saskatchewan is in the Cypress Hills – 1,392 metres (4,567 feet) above sea level. The highest parts of the Cypress Hills, along with sections of the Wood Mountain Hills, were the only parts of Saskatchewan not covered by glaciers during the last Ice Age.

Conglomerate Cliffs, Cypress Hills.

Karpan Photo

Question

Where are the largest active sand dunes in Canada?

a) Athabasca Sand Dunes
b) Douglas Provincial Park
c) Good Spirit Lake Provincial Park
d) Great Sand Hills
e) Manito Sand Hills

Answer

a) The Athabasca Sand Dunes stretch for approximately 100 km along the south shore of Lake Athabasca in northwest Saskatchewan. They are the largest active dune fields in Canada, and the largest this far north anywhere in the world. The two largest dune fields are the William River dune field west of the William River, covering 166 sq km (64 sq miles) and the Thomson Bay dune field on the south shore of the lake, covering 97 sq km (37 sq miles). Other smaller dune fields occur along the south shore and near the MacFarlane River. The dunes were formed as retreating glaciers deposited sandstone sediments in the spillways of the MacFarlane and William Rivers. As the glacial lake receded, the wind worked the sand into dunes.

According to a local Dene legend, the dunes were created when a giant man speared a giant beaver that thrashed its powerful tail around so much in the throes of death that it ground the surrounding soil into sand.

In 1992, Athabasca Sand Dunes Provincial Wilderness Park was established to protect and preserve the dunes, rare plants, and the spectacular scenery.

All of the other places listed in the question contain significant areas of sand dunes.

Athabasca Sand Dunes.   Karpan Photo

Question

70-mile Butte is a large promontory rising 100 metres above the valley floor in Grasslands National Park. How did it get its name?

a) It's 70 miles to the nearest water.
b) It's 70 miles to Fort Walsh.
c) It's 70 miles to the Canada/USA border.
d) It's 70 miles to the nearest trees.
e) It's 70 miles from Wood Mountain.

Answer

e) 70-mile Butte was named because it is 70 miles from Wood Mountain along the former North West Mounted Police patrol trail to Fort Walsh. The butte is the highest point of land in the region, and is a popular place for hiking (careful you don't step on a rattlesnake).

Question

Name Saskatchewan's highest waterfall (in a single drop).

a) Nistowiak Falls
b) Hunt Falls
c) Smoothrock Falls
d) MacFarlane River Falls
e) Elizabeth Falls

Answer

b) Hunt Falls (also known as Lefty's Falls) on the Grease River north of Lake Athabasca has the largest single drop – approximately 15 metres (almost 50 feet). The falls are also 60 metres (197 feet) wide. Along a three-kilometre stretch, which includes Hunt Falls, the Grease River drops 35 metres (115 feet). The falls are set in spectacular Precambrian Shield wilderness, surrounded by high cliffs and forested hills, and were named after W.E.D. Hunt, a Royal Canadian Naval Reserve Stoker First Class, who died in World War II.

All of the above choices are impressive Saskatchewan waterfalls, however none has as high a single drop as Hunt Falls.

Hunt Falls.   Karpan Photo

Question

Why is a community in northeast Saskatchewan called Southend?

a) It's at the southern end of the Athabasca basin where the rivers flow north.
b) It's at the southern end of Reindeer Lake.
c) It was the southernmost Hudson's Bay Company trading post during the fur trade.
d) It was named by Sir John Franklin for the southernmost point on his expedition to find the Northwest Passage.
e) It's at the southern end of Wollaston Lake.

Answer

b) It's at the southern end of Reindeer Lake.

Question

Why is a town in southwest Saskatchewan called Eastend?

a) It's at the east end of the Cypress Hills.
b) It was the traditional eastern boundary of the Blackfoot Confederacy.
c) It was at the eastern end of the District of Assiniboia.
d) It was at the eastern end of the District of Alberta.
e) It was the eastern terminus of the CPR's western Canada division.

Answer

a) It's at the east end of the Cypress Hills.

Lakes and Rivers

Question ✓

Of the ten largest freshwater lakes in North America, which
two are found in Saskatchewan?

a) Lac La Ronge
b) Lake Athabasca
c) Cree Lake
d) Reindeer Lake
e) Wollaston Lake

Answer

b, d) Lake Athabasca at 7,935 sq km is the ninth largest lake,
and Reindeer Lake at 6,650 sq km is the tenth largest lake in
North America.

Lake Athabasca is also the fourth largest lake completely
within the borders of Canada. North America's eight largest
lakes in order of size are: Lake Superior, Lake Huron, Lake
Michigan, Great Bear Lake, Great Slave Lake, Lake Erie, Lake
Winnipeg, and Lake Ontario.

Question

Name the largest lake entirely within Saskatchewan's borders.

a) Reindeer Lake
b) Lake Athabasca
c) Wollaston Lake
d) Lac La Ronge
e) Cree Lake

Answer

c) Wollaston Lake, covering 2,681 sq km, is the largest lake entirely within Saskatchewan. Cree Lake ranks second with 1,434 sq km and Lac La Ronge a close third at 1,413 sq km. Reindeer Lake and Lake Athabasca are both larger, although they extend beyond Saskatchewan's borders. About 30% of Lake Athabasca is in Alberta, and a small part of Reindeer Lake stretches into Manitoba.

Question

Where does the Qu'Appelle River begin?

a) Buffalo Pound Lake
b) Qu'Appelle Dam at Lake Diefenbaker
c) Fort Qu'Appelle
d) Qu'Appelle
e) Pasqua Lake

Answer

b) The Qu'Appelle River begins at the Qu'Appelle Dam on the east end of Lake Diefenbaker. It meanders across more than half of Saskatchewan for about 430 km, joining the Assiniboine River just across the Saskatchewan/Manitoba border.

Question ✓

Name the Saskatchewan lake where the specific gravity of the water is greater than that of the Dead Sea, and where it is impossible to sink.

Answer

Little Manitou Lake near Watrous is rich in minerals such as sodium, magnesium and potassium, and is so buoyant that you can float with ease while sitting and reading your newspaper.

The water is said to cure whatever ails you. Plains Indians brought their sick to this "lake of good spirit", early settlers hauled the healing water home by the barrel-full, and a steady stream of tourists turned the tiny resort community of Manitou Beach into the "Carlsbad of Canada". The village's centrepiece is Manitou Springs Mineral Spa which claims to have the largest indoor mineral pool in Canada.

Little Manitou Lake.

Karpan Photo

Question

Which Saskatchewan lake is said to have a resident sea monster?

a) Turtle Lake
b) Candle Lake
c) Black Bear Island Lake
d) Pelican Lake
e) Loch Leven

Answer

a) Turtle Lake. Stories about the mysterious Turtle Lake Monster have been around as long as anyone can remember. Some say it has a head like a horse, a dog, or a pig. It's been described as having fins like a fish, or humps like a camel. Skeptics argue that the "monster" is nothing more than a large sturgeon, but many who have seen it insist that this is no mere fish.

There's the story of the police diver who went into the lake looking for a drowned man but refused to go down again because of what he had seen. Or the girl who was haunted by the large eye of a creature she accidentally stepped on while getting out of a boat, thinking she was stepping on a log.

The elusive monster has been sighted from a restaurant window, from airplanes and motor boats. Those who have tried to chase the creature by boat have always been out-run.

Question ✓

Which major river flows west out of Saskatchewan?

a) Churchill
b) Clearwater
c) Grease
d) Montreal
e) Cree

Answer

b) The Clearwater River flows south from its headwaters in Broach Lake in northwest Saskatchewan, then turns west, emptying into the Athabasca River at Fort McMurray, Alberta.

Question

How many kilometres of shoreline does Lake Diefenbaker have?

a) 300 km
b) 500 km
c) 800 km
d) 1,000 km
e) 1,200 km

Answer

c) Although difficult to measure exactly, Lake Diefenbaker has approximately 800 km of shoreline. Part of the South Saskatchewan River system, Lake Diefenbaker is a reservoir that was created with the completion of Gardiner Dam in 1967.

Question

How many cubic metres of earth were moved to form the reservoir of Lake Diefenbaker?

a) 25 million
b) 42 million
c) 63 million
d) 85 million
e) 100 million

Answer

e) 100 million. Construction began on Gardiner Dam on the South Saskatchewan River in 1959 and continued until 1967 when the reservoir known as Lake Diefenbaker began to fill. One hundred million cubic metres of earth were moved during the project, creating one of the largest earth-fill dams in the world. Lake Diefenbaker provides drinking water to many communities, water for irrigation, recreation, and industry, and is used to produce electricity at Coteau Creek power station.

Gardiner Dam.   Karpan Photo

Question

Which lake is home to Grey Owl's cabin?

a) Amisk Lake
b) Ajawaan Lake
c) Atton's Lake
d) Athabasca Lake
e) Anglin Lake

Answer

b) Grey Owl and his wife Anahereo moved into their log cabin called Beaver Lodge on the shore of Ajawaan Lake in Prince Albert National Park in 1931. They had been invited by the national park so Grey Owl could continue his conservation work and writings, and provide publicity for the newly-formed park.

Grey Owl, whose real name was Archibald Belaney, was born in 1888 in Hastings, England. In 1906, he immigrated to Canada to fulfill his dream of living the life of an Indian.

Anahereo helped turn his attentions towards conservation, especially of beavers, whose numbers were dwindling after years of trapping. Grey Owl began writing articles and books, and speaking about nature and wildlife conservation.

Following a busy speaking tour of Britain, Grey Owl caught pneumonia and died in 1938. Almost immediately, word broke about his English origins and how he had misled everyone into believing he was an Indian. Imposter or not, his message of conservation still lives on.

Grey Owl's cabin, along with one built later for Anahereo, has been preserved by the park and is a popular destination for hundreds of visitors each year. Grey Owl, Anahereo, and their daughter, Shirley Dawn, are buried together nearby.

Grey Owl's cabin.   Karpan Photo

Question

Which Saskatchewan lake is the largest in the world to drain naturally into two different oceans?

a) Wollaston Lake
b) Lake Athabasca
c) Cree Lake
d) Lac La Ronge
e) Selwyn Lake

Answer

a) The northwest corner of Wollaston Lake is where the Fond du Lac River begins. It winds northwest to Black Lake then Lake Athabasca, which drains north to the Arctic Ocean.

The Cochrane River begins on the northern end of Wollaston Lake, eventually flowing into Reindeer Lake which drains towards Hudson Bay.

Question

How did Old Wives Lake get its name?

a) A group of early settlers was travelling across the lake in winter when two elderly women drowned after falling through thin ice.
b) Blackfoot women traditionally came here to tan hides of buffalo killed in the hunt.
c) Cree women kept campfires burning here while the rest of the band escaped from a Blackfoot attack.
d) Cree women were traditionally buried near the lake.
e) The story of the lake's name is considered an old wives' tale.

Answer

c) A Cree legend tells of buffalo hunters who were on their way to their camp in the Qu'Appelle Valley with their processed meat when they were spotted by Blackfoot scouts.

Anticipating an attack from the Blackfoot the next day, an old woman suggested that the elderly women remain in camp and keep the fires burning all night while the rest of the party escaped under cover of darkness. The burning fires would trick the Blackfoot into believing that the entire camp was still there.

When the Blackfoot attacked the next morning and discovered that they had been tricked, they killed all the old women. It is said that the laughter of the old women can still be heard at the lake on windy nights.

Question

Which is longer, the North Saskatchewan River or the South Saskatchewan River?

Answer

The South Saskatchewan River is longer, measuring 1,392 kilometres from where it begins at the confluence of the Bow and Oldman Rivers in southern Alberta, to its confluence with the North Saskatchewan River just east of Prince Albert. The river flows east past Medicine Hat, then is joined by the Red Deer River just past the Alberta/Saskatchewan border. It widens into Lake Diefenbaker, then flows north through Saskatoon, and northeast to where it joins the North Saskatchewan River. It also has the larger flow, averaging approximately 280 cubic metres per second.

The North Saskatchewan River flows for 1,287 kilometres and has an average discharge of 245 cubic metres per second. Beginning in the Columbia Icefield in Alberta, the river winds through Rocky Mountain House and Edmonton in Alberta, then to North Battleford and Prince Albert, joining the South Saskatchewan River about 50 kilometres east of Prince Albert.

South Saskatchewan River near Batoche.   Karpan Photo

On the Wild Side

Question

How many bird species have been confirmed in Saskatchewan?

Answer

At the time of publication, Nature Saskatchewan's Field Checklist of Saskatchewan Birds had a confirmed species list of 364.

"Confirmed" means that the bird has been identified through a specimen, a photograph or a sound recording. The list includes birds which breed here, which migrate through, and a few "stragglers" which do not occur regularly. You can no longer see two birds on this list – the passenger pigeon is extinct, and the greater prairie chicken has been extirpated, meaning that the bird still exists but no longer exists in Saskatchewan.

In addition, Saskatchewan has 66 hypothetical bird species based on unconfirmed reports. Together, the Saskatchewan bird list has 430 species.

Question

How many ducks are there in Saskatchewan?

a) 500,000
b) 1 million
c) 4 million
d) 7 million
e) 12 million

Answer

d) Wildlife surveys have put the long-term average duck population in Saskatchewan at 7.4 million. To put this in perspective, that's close to 30% of Canada's duck population of 25 million. Almost one in four ducks in North America is raised in Saskatchewan. It's for good reason that Saskatchewan is referred to as "North America's Duck Factory".

Green-winged teal.

Karpan Photo

Question

How many species of snakes occur in Saskatchewan?

a) 3
b) 5
c) 7
d) 9
e) 12

Answer

d) According to the Canadian Wildlife Service, nine species of snakes are found in Saskatchewan. They can be divided into the following categories:

- Striped snakes: Red-sided garter snake, Plains garter snake, Wandering garter snake
- Brown and blotched snakes: Bullsnake, Plains hognose snake, Prairie rattlesnake
- Colorful snakes: Eastern yellowbelly racer, Smooth green snake, Northern redbelly snake

The Prairie rattlesnake is the only poisonous snake in Saskatchewan. It is found primarily in the Frenchman River Valley in and around Grasslands National Park, and along the South Saskatchewan River close to the Alberta border.

Prairie rattlesnake.   Karpan Photo

Question

Which snake is the most abundant in the province?

Answer

The Plains garter snake is found throughout the southern half of Saskatchewan, commonly in wet meadows, parks, open grasslands, and farm yards. It has a bright orange stripe running along its back, and side stripes that vary in color from cream to yellow. Plains garter snakes can measure anywhere from 50-100 cm (20-40 inches).

Question

How far north have snakes been reported in Saskatchewan?

Answer

Red-sided garter snakes have been recorded as far north as Cluff Lake – about 80 km south of Lake Athabasca.

Question

Where would you go in Saskatchewan to watch gopher races?

Answer

It's been a long-standing tradition in Eston to celebrate Canada Day on July 1 with the World Super Gopher Derby. Gophers (or Richardson's ground squirrels for the technical purists) are rounded up from nearby fields a day or two before the big event. On July 1 they are placed in a specially designed race track to see which one makes it first to the finish line. After the race, all the gophers are set free.

Question

Which of the following animals are currently found in the wild in Saskatchewan?

a) bison
b) woodland caribou
c) barren-ground caribou
d) grizzly bears
e) pronghorn antelope

Answer

a, b, c, e) All except grizzly bears. Bison are found in the wild in Prince Albert National Park, primarily in the southwest near the Sturgeon River. Small herds of woodland caribou are found in various parts of the north, and barren-ground caribou from the tundra migrate into the far northern part of Saskatchewan for the winter. Pronghorn antelope are found in southern Saskatchewan, primarily in the southeast. Grizzly bears once lived in Saskatchewan, but are no longer found here.

Pronghorn antelope.

Karpan Photo

Question

Has a polar bear ever been seen in the wild in Saskatchewan?

Answer

Yes. On September 4, 1999, sport fishermen on Burnett Lake (near the 59th parallel, close to the Manitoba border), spotted something white in the water. At first they thought it was a gull. But as they approached in their small boat, they were surprised to find a polar bear – swimming directly towards them! After taking a few seconds of video, they quickly motored away.

Wildlife biologists who saw the video confirmed that this was in fact a polar bear, probably a sub-adult male. This was the first confirmed sighting of a polar bear in Saskatchewan.

Burnett Lake is some 400 km from Hudson Bay, the bears' normal habitat, where they feed on seals. This lost bear was likely getting quite hungry, so a couple of fishermen probably looked like a reasonable substitute for seals.

Question

Who became famous for the phrase "Remember you belong to nature, not it to you"?

Answer

It was Grey Owl, who spent many years in Prince Albert National Park writing about the wilderness. He is considered one of Canada's foremost naturalists and conservationists.

Question

Canada's only black-tailed prairie dogs in their native habitat are found near this community:

a) Avonlea
b) Val Marie
c) Leader
d) Kindersley
e) Carnduff

Answer

b) The countryside near Val Marie, in and around Grasslands National Park, is the only part of Canada to have black-tailed prairie dogs. They range across the plains and plateaus of North America, from this tiny part of southern Saskatchewan to northern Mexico. Larger than gophers (or Richardson's ground squirrels to be technically correct), prairie dogs live in sophisticated colonies on the grasslands. They frequently stand upright on top of the entrance to their burrows, watching for predators such as hawks that may be circling overhead. They often make squealing noises when danger is near, before disappearing to the safety of their burrows.

Black-tailed prairie dog.

Karpan Photo

Question

The first bird sanctuary in North America was established at:

a) Redberry Lake
b) Opuntia Lake
c) Foam Lake
d) Last Mountain Lake
e) Quill Lakes

Answer

d) The northern end of Last Mountain Lake was set aside by the federal government as a bird sanctuary in 1887. Now administered as Last Mountain Lake National Wildlife Area, the sanctuary is a haven for more than 280 species of birds that enjoy its shallow wetlands, grasslands, and trees. During fall migration, the lake is used as a staging area for thousands of sandhill cranes, Canada geese and snow geese on their journey south. Endangered whooping cranes also stop here during their migration.

Migrating snow geese, Last Mountain Lake.　　　　Karpan Photo

Question

Where in Saskatchewan did a hunter shoot a white-tailed deer which set a new world record for the largest white-tailed deer antlers?

a) Broderick
b) Bengough
c) Broadview
d) Biggar
e) Balcarres

Answer

d) Milo Hanson shot the deer on his own land near Biggar on November 23, 1993. A monument commemorating the record now stands in the town of Biggar.

Monument to Hanson Buck, Biggar.　　　　　Karpan Photo

Question

What part of Saskatchewan has 10 plants that grow nowhere else in the world?

a) Grasslands National Park
b) Athabasca Sand Dunes
c) Cypress Hills
d) Quill Lakes
e) Duck Mountain Provincial Park

Answer

b) The Athabasca Sand Dunes has five broad-leaved herbs, four willows and one grass that are endemic, meaning that they are restricted to this area and are found nowhere else on Earth. Scientists say that it is rare for a northern area to have this many endemic plants. Why they developed here is still considered an evolutionary puzzle. In addition to the 10 endemics, the Athabasca Sand Dunes has another 42 plants considered rare in Saskatchewan.

The inland sea thrift is one of 10 endemic plants found in the Athabasca Sand Dunes.

Karpan Photo

115

Question

Where can you see what is believed to be the largest tree in Saskatchewan measured by diameter?

a) Prince Albert National Park
b) Near Cumberland House
c) Near La Ronge
d) Near Blaine Lake
e) Near Hudson Bay

Answer

d) With a diameter of 1.55 metres (61 inches), this huge tree is located southeast of Blaine Lake near the former Laird ferry crossing on the North Saskatchewan River. A cross between a plains cottonwood and balsam poplar, it has a girth measuring 4.8 metres (over 16 feet), bark 10 cm (4 inches) thick, and is estimated to be between 100 and 150 years old. It is not

particularly high, measuring 21 metres (almost 69 feet), with branches spanning 32 metres (104.5 feet).

The tree was nominated for record diameter for the Saskatchewan Forestry Association's *Saskatchewan Trees of Renown*. The association indicated that they are not aware of reports of any other trees with a larger diameter in Saskatchewan.

The "big tree" near Blaine Lake.
Karpan Photo

Question

Where can you see what is believed to be the tallest white spruce tree in Saskatchewan?

a) Nisbet Forest
b) Porcupine Hills
c) Prince Albert National Park
d) Bronson Forest
e) Meadow Lake Provincial Park

Answer

c) The tallest recorded white spruce, with a height of 37 metres (121.4 feet), is on the Treebeard Hiking Trail in Prince Albert National Park.

According to *Saskatchewan Trees of Renown*, published in 1985 by the Saskatchewan Forestry Association, this tree has a diameter of 61.5 centimetres (24.2 inches). It is approximately 120 years old.

Along the Treebeard Hiking Trail you have a chance to see other giant trees including balsam poplar and balsam fir. Ideal growing conditions with nutrient-rich soil and a high water table have contributed to their amazing sizes.

Question

While Grey Owl and his wife Anahereo were at Prince Albert National Park, they had two pet beavers which became celebrities. What were the beavers' names?

a) Jelly Roll
b) Donut
c) Riptide
d) Rawhide
e) Bismark
f) Crumpet

Answer

a, d) When Grey Owl and Anahereo moved to Prince Albert National Park in 1931, they took along their two pet beavers Jelly Roll (a female) and Rawhide (a male).

The beavers quickly became accustomed to their new surroundings, constructing part of their lodge over a plunge hole in the floor of Grey Owl's cabin. Rawhide and Jelly Roll often brought branches and debris through the cabin door to add to their lodge, which occupied about one-third of the cabin.

When visitors came to see Grey Owl, he would often call upon the beavers to perform a few tricks, then reward them with apples (their favorite food), peanuts or other treats.

Question

Where is Saskatchewan's first World Biosphere Reserve?

a) Redberry Lake
b) Last Mountain Lake
c) Prince Albert National Park
d) Cypress Hills
e) Grasslands National Park

Answer

a) Redberry Lake (including its watershed, the nearby community of Hafford, and most of the surrounding rural municipality) was designated by the United Nations (UNESCO) as a World Biosphere Reserve on January 21, 2000.

A biosphere reserve is a natural environment where conservation takes place along with sustained economic use of resources. Natural aspects of the biosphere reserve include Redberry Lake and its islands, wetlands, grasslands, and aspen groves. Research and education are facilitated by the Redberry Pelican Project which monitors birds including American White Pelicans and more than 180 other species at the Redberry Lake bird sanctuary. The Stuart Houston Ecology Centre at Redberry Lake Regional Park features videos of activity on pelican nesting islands, and other nature exhibits.

Pelicans are Redberry Lake's most famous residents.   Karpan Photo

A Peek at Parks

Question ✓

The following are some of Saskatchewan's most popular provincial parks. Which three get the most visitors each year?

a) Meadow Lake
b) Saskatchewan Landing
c) Duck Mountain
d) Cypress Hills
e) Good Spirit Lake
f) Lac La Ronge
g) Moose Mountain
h) Douglas
i) Greenwater Lake

Answer

a, d, g) Saskatchewan Environment indicates that Meadow Lake, Cypress Hills and Moose Mountain provincial parks are consistently the three that get the most visitors, although their order within the top three varies from year to year.

In 2001, for example, Meadow Lake had 246,316 visitors, Moose Mountain had 196,330 visitors, and Cypress Hills had 181,793 visitors.

Question ✓

Name the largest provincial park in Saskatchewan.

Answer

Lac La Ronge Provincial Park is the largest, with an area of 336,200 ha (830,400 acres).

Question ✓

Which provincial park has more water than land base?

Answer

Lac La Ronge Provincial Park has more water than land. The park encompasses a hundred or so lakes in addition to massive Lac La Ronge itself.

Question

Waskesiu is the name for both the resort village and adjoining lake in Prince Albert National Park. "Waskesiu" is derived from a Cree word meaning:

a) Big lake
b) Red deer
c) Wolf country
d) Thick forest
e) Bountiful wildlife

Answer

b) Waskesiu is derived from a Cree word meaning red deer, referring to elk which were plentiful in the area.

Question

Prince Albert National Park was formed in large part because of a political favor owed by a prime minister. Which prime minister gave the order to establish the park?

a) Louis St. Laurent
b) William Lyon Mackenzie King
c) John Diefenbaker
d) Lester Pearson
e) Arthur Meighen

Answer

b) In the 1925 general election, the Liberals formed a minority government, but Prime Minister Mackenzie King lost his Ontario seat. The Liberal MP for Prince Albert, Charles McDonald, gave up his seat so that King could run in a by-election. This was seen as good news for Prince Albert. What better way to get federal concessions than from a prime minister in need of local support?

Prince Albert had previously been unsuccessful in lobbying the government to establish a national park, so now King was asked to make the park a priority. Prince Albert supported King, who won the by-election, then a few months later won the 1926 general election, giving the Liberals a majority. King handily won the Prince Albert riding, defeating a young political upstart by the name of John Diefenbaker.

King made good on his promise for a park, despite objections from federal park bureaucrats who resented political interference.

Question

The Goodwin House, a two-storey stone home that dates to 1900, is found in this provincial park:

a) Greenwater Lake Provincial Park
b) Saskatchewan Landing Provincial Park
c) Pike Lake Provincial Park
d) Meadow Lake Provincial Park
e) Katepwa Provincial Park

Answer

b) The Goodwin House is in Saskatchewan Landing Provincial Park, on the south side of Lake Diefenbaker on Hwy. #4. It was built by Frank Goodwin, a North West Mounted Police officer, and for many years served as a stopping place for settlers travelling between Swift Current and Battleford on the Battleford Trail. The restored building now serves as the park visitor centre, and houses displays on flora and fauna.

Goodwin House. Karpan Photo

Readin' and Writin'

Question

The fictional community of Crocus, Saskatchewan was immortalized by W.O. Mitchell in his classic novel and radio series *Jake and the Kid*. Which real community served as the model for Crocus?

a) Arcola
b) Alida
c) Carnduff
d) Carlyle
e) Weyburn

Answer

e) W.O. Mitchell's home town of Weyburn provided much of the inspiration for the fictional town of Crocus. Mitchell became widely acclaimed for his down-to-earth portrayals of prairie life.

Mitchell became a household name as his weekly series of 320 radio dramas based on *Jake and the Kid* ran on CBC radio between 1950 and 1956. His books *Jake and the Kid*, *Who Has Seen the Wind*, along with dramas including *The Devil's Instrument* and *The Black Bonspiel of Wullie MacCrimmon* have become Canadian classics. Mitchell died in 1998.

Question

Name the Saskatchewan-born author known for his humorous books *Why Shoot the Teacher?*, *Never Sleep Three in a Bed*, and *The Night We Stole the Mountie's Car*.

Answer

Max Braithwaite, born in Nokomis, became one of Canada's best-loved humorists. An author, playwright, and script writer, Braithwaite was recognized nationally when he was awarded the Leacock Memorial Medal for Humour in 1972 for his novel *The Night We Stole the Mountie's Car*.

Question

Which community in southwest Saskatchewan was known as "Whitemud" in Wallace Stegner's classic book *Wolf Willow*?

a) Ravenscrag
b) Eastend
c) Shaunavon
d) Maple Creek
e) Avonlea

Answer

b) Whitemud was actually the town of Eastend, located at the foot of the Cypress Hills. It was here that the Stegner family homesteaded from 1914 to 1920, and where young Wallace developed a deep appreciation for the landscape, culture and history of the area. Published in 1963, the book (named for the aromatic wolf willow shrub) combines history, fiction, and memories of Wallace's boyhood years growing up in the pioneer community. The Stegner home at 126 Tamarack Street is now used as a writer's retreat.

Question

Where is North America's largest collection of 13th to 17th century books?

Answer

Athol Murray College of Notre Dame in Wilcox, Saskatchewan. The College Archives/Museum has a remarkable collection of over 400 rare books and manuscripts, all of which were the personal collection of college founder, Father Athol Murray.

Many of the ancient books belonged to Father Bacciochi, a Corsican priest and grand-nephew of Napoleon Bonaparte. Father Bacciochi moved to Saskatchewan in 1918 and worked here until his death in 1951. He willed his book collection to Father Murray.

Some of the books originated in the personal library of Lord Tweedsmuir, while others came from the library of General Robert E. Lee, of United States Civil War fame, whose granddaughter became a personal friend of Father Murray.

The collection includes three 13th-century manuscripts handwritten by monks on parchment and vellum, the *Chronicles of 1515* printed on the original Gutenberg Press, and an original 1535 *Martin Luther Bible*. The original *Nuremberg Chronicle*, published in 1493, tells the story of mankind from Creation to 1492. The *Works of St. Augustine* (first edition) from 1489 has a wooden cover covered with sheepskin. Other works include an original book by Erasmus dating to 1516, a book by St. Thomas Aquinas dating to 1481, and a handwritten decree by King James I in 1603, complete with original royal wax seal.

Nuremberg Chronicle.　　　Athol Murray College of Notre Dame Archives

Question

Name the Saskatchewan author who twice won the Governor General's Literary Award for Fiction – once for the book *Man Descending*, and later for the book, *The Englishman's Boy*.

a) Max Braithwaite
b) Lois Simmie
c) Ken Mitchell
d) Guy Vanderhaeghe
e) Bonnie Burnard

Answer

d) Guy Vanderhaeghe won the award in 1982 for his collection of short stories entitled *Man Descending*. In 1996, he again won the award for his novel *The Englishman's Boy*.

Question

Where was the first newspaper published west of Winnipeg?

a) Pelly
b) Battleford
c) Cumberland House
d) Prince Albert
e) Regina

Answer

b) The first newspaper was published in Battleford by Patrick Gammie Laurie. With a background in the newspaper business, Laurie longed for the challenge of publishing a newspaper where none had been published before. He loaded his printing press and belongings onto four Red River carts and set out from Fort Garry (Winnipeg) to Battleford, the new capital of the North-West Territories. The first edition of the paper, the *Saskatchewan Herald*, came out on August 25, 1878.

P.G. Laurie in front of the Saskatchewan Herald *office, Battleford.*
Saskatchewan Archives S-B 75

The Entertainers

Question

Which Saskatchewan-born singer/songwriter wrote the songs *Universal Soldier*, *Up Where We Belong*, and *Until It's Time For You to Go?*

Answer

Buffy Saint-Marie was born on the Piapot Reserve in Saskatchewan. She wrote *Universal Soldier* in the 1960s and it became a hit when Donovan recorded it in 1965. *Up Where We Belong* was written for the film *An Officer and a Gentleman*, and won an Academy Award. *Until It's Time For You to Go* was recorded by several artists including Elvis Presley, Barbara Streisand, and Neil Diamond.

Question

Which singer-songwriter, raised in Saskatoon, wrote the hit songs *Both Sides Now*, *Big Yellow Taxi*, and *Circle Game?*

Answer

Joni Mitchell was born in Fort Macleod, Alberta but grew up in Saskatoon. On the cover of her 1969 album *Clouds*, Joni is shown holding a western red lily, Saskatchewan's floral emblem.

Question

The Saskatchewan Arts Board was the first arms-length government arts funding agency in North America.

a) True
b) False

Answer

a) True. Founded in 1948 during T.C. Douglas' tenure as premier, the Saskatchewan Arts Board was conceived to support and develop arts and culture in the province. It grew out of a cultural resurgence that occurred after World War II as prosperity gradually returned to the economy.

The Saskatchewan Arts Board supports many disciplines including visual arts, music, literature, drama, handcrafts, and film. The Board influenced the development of institutions such as the Canada Council and the U.S. National Endowment for the Arts.

Question

Name the Saskatchewan-born actor who played the wily bootlegger Albert Golo in the television series *North of 60*.

Answer

It was Gordon Tootoosis who portrayed Albert Golo. Born on the Poundmaker Reserve near Cut Knife, Tootoosis has also made television appearances on shows such as *MacGyver*, *Northern Exposure*, and *Black Robe*, and in the mini-series *Big Bear*.

Question

Which community is home to the longest running short film and video festival in Canada?

a) Melville
b) Melfort
c) Saskatoon
d) Yorkton
e) Regina

Answer

d) The Yorkton Short Film and Video Festival was established in 1947, making it the longest running festival of its kind in Canada. Canadian productions running 60 minutes or less are eligible for Golden Sheaf Awards in categories such as best drama, documentary, science/nature, comedy, and education, as well as for best art direction, editing, script, and many other categories. The prestigious Golden Sheaf Award of Excellence is presented to the most outstanding production entered in the festival. Awards are also given to international entries.

Golden Sheaf Award.

Karpan Photo

Question

Which symphony orchestra is the longest continuously performing symphony orchestra in Canada?

a) Saskatoon Symphony Orchestra
b) Regina Symphony Orchestra

Answer

b) The Regina Symphony holds the honor of being Canada's longest continuously performing symphony orchestra. The forerunner of the symphony was the Regina Orchestral Society which staged its first concert on December 3, 1908 in City Hall Auditorium, with Franklin Laubach conducting.

Today, the Regina Symphony Orchestra (RSO) consists of 55 - 60 professional musicians led by Music Director/Conductor, Maestro Victor Sawa. The RSO and the Regina Symphony Chamber Players present dozens of concerts every year through their various series such as Masterworks, Shumiatcher Pops, Government House, James Kurtz Baroque & Beyond, and Little Masters Concert Series. They also present special Christmas and Remembrance Day concerts, host the New Music Festival, perform for government functions and deliver an extensive school-concert program reaching over 10,000 children.

With a mandate to bring the music to the people, the RSO has performed at Buffalo Pound Provincial Park, as well as at some rather unconventional locations, such as a brew pub and on a floating barge on Wascana Lake.

Question

Name the Saskatchewan-born actor known for his comedy performances in movies such as *Airplane*, and *Naked Gun*.

Answer

Leslie Nielsen was born in Regina in 1926. He studied acting in Toronto and New York City, and eventually made his way to Hollywood where he earned a reputation as a comedy actor for his deadpan performances. He has appeared in over 80 movies and has made more than 1,500 appearances on television.

Question

Which festival bills itself as the world's largest Ukrainian cabaret?

Answer

The Vesna Festival, held in Saskatoon, features traditional Ukrainian dancing, music, entertainment, and cultural displays.

Vesna Festival.

Karpan Photo

Question

Saskatchewan is home to the second longest continuously running stage production in Canada. Which production is it?

Answer

The *Trial of Louis Riel* has been staged annually in Regina since 1967, making it Canada's second longest continuously running stage production (*Anne of Green Gables* has been running slightly longer). The *Trial* is a dramatic re-enactment of the original proceedings when Métis leader Louis Riel was tried for treason following his involvement with the Northwest Rebellion of 1885. The production takes place each summer in the Shumiatcher Theatre of the MacKenzie Art Gallery.

Scene from "The Trial of Louis Riel".　　　　　　　Karpan Photo

Weathering the Storm

Question

The largest hail stone to fall in Canada fell near Cedoux, Saskatchewan in August, 1973. How much did the hail stone weigh?

a) 110 grams (.24 lb)
b) 150 grams (.33 lb)
c) 215 grams (.47 lb)
d) 290 grams (.64 lb)
e) 340 grams (.75 lb)

Answer

d) A major storm swept through southeast Saskatchewan, with the largest recorded hail stone falling near Cedoux, north of Weyburn. It weighed a whopping 290 grams, or almost two-thirds of a pound. The hailstone also measured 114 mm in diameter, almost 4.5 inches, about the size of a grapefruit.

Question

Which Saskatchewan community was hit by a tornado that is considered the worst ever in Canada for loss of life?

a) Weyburn
b) Regina
c) Bengough
d) Wakaw
e) Lloydminster

Answer

b) The Regina Tornado of June 30, 1912 resulted in 28 dead and hundreds injured. Looking at the horrific damage, observers considered it a miracle that more were not killed. The tornado came from the south, crossed Wascana Lake then laid a path of destruction to Victoria Park and downtown.

The strangest story was that of two men canoeing on Wascana Lake. Their canoe was picked up by the wind and twirled around. One man was thrown out and killed. The canoe landed right side up and rescuers found the other man still sitting in the canoe, his hand still grasping the paddle.

One of the most tragic stories was that of Frank and Bertha Blenkhorn. On the day of the tornado, they were caught in the open in Victoria Park and died when they were hurled against a building. Married in England in early April, the Blenkhorns made their way to Regina later that month.

Aftermath of the Regina Tornado.   Saskatchewan Archives R-A 868

Question

Southern Saskatchewan is one of the driest parts of Canada.
But on May 30, 1961, a storm in Buffalo Gap in south-central
Saskatchewan set a Canadian record for rainfall within one
hour. Approximately how much rain fell within one hour?

a) 50 mm or 2 inches
b) 100 mm or 4 inches
c) 150 mm or 6 inches
d) 200 mm or 8 inches
e) 250 mm or 10 inches

Answer

e) 250 mm or 10 inches. Roads were washed out, fields were
eroded and crops stripped of vegetation. Bark was stripped
from trees and paint stripped from buildings.

Question

Which community calls itself the "Blizzard Capital of Saskatchewan"?

a) Kennedy
b) Kinistino
c) Kyle
d) Kelvington
e) Kenaston

Answer

e) The village of Kenaston on Hwy. #11 calls itself the Blizzard Capital of Saskatchewan. The Chamber of Commerce came up with the name following a particularly bad blizzard in 1978. More than 100 people ended up storm-stayed in the village, and spent the night in the local Catholic church or billeted with families. The snowfall was so heavy that visitors had to be shuttled around on snowmobiles. The rink roof collapsed

under the weight of the snow.

In recognition of Kenaston's title, a 5.5-metre (18-foot) fibreglass snowman was built in a park on the west end of the village near the railway tracks.

Karpan Photo

Question

Which Saskatchewan community is considered the sunniest place in Canada?

a) Eastend
b) Estevan
c) Saskatoon
d) Swift Current
e) Regina

Answer

b) Estevan bills itself as the "Sunshine Capital of Canada" for good reason. According to Environment Canada, Estevan has the greatest average annual number of sunny hours – 2,537.

Question

Which community holds the record for the highest precipitation in one year?

a) Kamsack
b) Hudson Bay
c) Lloydminster
d) Cree Lake
e) La Loche

Answer

a) In 1921, Kamsack received 916 mm (36.6 inches) of precipitation. This part of eastern Saskatchewan normally gets less than half that amount of precipitation in a year.

Question

Which two Saskatchewan communities hold the record for the highest temperature ever recorded in Canada?

a) Swift Current and Maple Creek
b) Rosetown and Kindersley
c) Shaunavon and Val Marie
d) Midale and Yellowgrass
e) Estevan and Oxbow

Answer

d) Midale and Yellowgrass. On July 5, 1937, the thermometer hit 45 degrees C (113 degrees F). Midale is between Weyburn and Estevan, and Yellowgrass is just northwest of Weyburn. On the same day, the temperature in Regina hit 43.3 degrees C (110 degrees F), setting a record for the highest temperature for capital cities in Canada.

Question

Which Saskatchewan community has the warmest annual average temperature?

a) Eston
b) Maple Creek
c) Assiniboia
d) Leader
e) Wynyard

Answer

b) The average annual temperature in Maple Creek is 5.4 degrees C (41.7 degrees F), the warmest in the province.

Question

Which community holds the record for the coldest temperature ever recorded in Saskatchewan?

a) Uranium City
b) La Ronge
c) Prince Albert
d) Saskatoon
e) Buffalo Narrows

Answer

c) On February 1, 1893, the temperature in Prince Albert fell to -56.7 degrees C (-70 degrees F). While Saskatchewan can get a tad chilly in winter, it doesn't hold the Canadian record. That honor belongs to Snag, Yukon which hit -63 degrees C (-81 degrees F) on February 3, 1947. According to Environment Canada, communities in Ontario, Alberta, British Columbia, and Northwest Territories also have record lows which surpass Prince Albert's.

Question

Which community holds the record for the highest snowfall in one year?

a) Uranium City
b) Prince Albert
c) Pelly
d) Meadow Lake
e) Pelican Narrows

Answer

c) During the winter of 1955-56, Pelly received 386 cm (12.7 feet) of snow.

Gone Fishin'

Question

What was the weight of the biggest fish ever caught in Saskatchewan?

Answer

In 1962, a 122.5 kg (270 pound) lake sturgeon was caught in the South Saskatchewan River. Since the population of sturgeon has declined in recent years, anglers are not currently permitted to keep sturgeon.

Question

Name the only place in Saskatchewan where you can fish for Largemouth bass.

Answer

The only place is Boundary Dam reservoir near Estevan. Water temperatures in Saskatchewan are generally too cool for Largemouth bass. However, since this reservoir is next to a coal-fired power station, the water is warm year round. The introduction of Largemouth bass was a pilot project which has proven successful. The largest bass caught and released here was a 61-cm (24-inch) fish weighing 3.6 kg (7.9 pounds).

Question

How many people fish in Saskatchewan?

a) 100,000
b) 180,000
c) 220,000
d) 270,000
e) 325,000

Answer

c) In 2002, approximately 222,000 people went fishing in Saskatchewan, including licensed adult anglers and children who do not require a licence. That's almost a quarter of the population of the province.

Question

How many species of game fish are pursued by anglers in Saskatchewan?

Answer

21. Arctic grayling, Brook trout, Brown trout, Bullhead, Burbot, Carp, Channel catfish, Cutthroat trout, Goldeye, Lake trout, Largemouth bass, Northern pike, Rainbow trout, Rock bass, Sauger, Splake, Lake sturgeon, Tiger trout, Walleye, Lake whitefish, Yellow perch.

Question

The most commonly caught fish in Saskatchewan is Northern pike. Approximately how many are caught each year by anglers?

a) 700,000
b) 1.2 million
c) 1.9 million
d) 2.6 million
e) 4.5 million

Answer

e) According to the most recent surveys, approximately 4.5 million Northern pike are caught by licensed anglers in Saskatchewan. This includes both kept fish and those live-released. Of the 4.5 million pike caught, just over 1 million are kept.

Question

What is the most commonly kept fish in Saskatchewan?

a) Northern pike
b) Yellow perch
c) Rainbow trout
d) Lake trout
e) Walleye

Answer

b) Saskatchewan anglers keep approximately 1.25 million Yellow perch each year.

Question

What is the length of the largest Northern pike caught and live-released by an angler in Saskatchewan?

Answer

A pike measuring 139.7 cm (55 inches) was caught and released in Lake Athabasca in August, 2002 by a guest of Athabasca Fishing Lodges. This was a new Northern pike record for Canada.

Question

What is the length of the largest Sauger caught and live-released by an angler in Saskatchewan?

Answer

A Sauger measuring 58 cm (23 inches) was caught and released at Tobin Lake in May, 2002.

Question

What is the length of the largest Brown trout caught and live-released by an angler in Saskatchewan?

Answer

A Brown trout measuring 74.3 cm (29.25 inches) was caught and released at Shannon Lake in 2001.

Question

Saskatchewan holds the record for the largest Lake trout in the world. How much did the fish weigh?

Answer

A Lake trout weighing 46.26 kg (102 pounds) was caught in the net of a commercial fisherman in Lake Athabasca on August 8, 1961.

World's largest Lake trout.   Saskatchewan Archives R-B 5125-1

Question

What is the record weight for a Walleye caught in Saskatchewan?

Answer

8.2 kg (18 pounds) caught in Tobin Lake in 1997.

Question

What is the largest Lake trout ever caught on a line and live released in Saskatchewan?

Answer

In July, 2002, Athabasca Fishing Lodges' guest Brad Spencer caught and released a Lake trout with a length of 137.2 cm (54 inches) and a girth of 86.4 cm (34 inches). It was estimated that the monstrous fish, caught in Lake Athabasca, weighed around 38 kg (83 pounds). This was a record not only for Saskatchewan, but for all of Canada.

Question

The Fort Qu'Appelle Fish Culture Station raises fish to stock waterbodies throughout the province. Approximately how many fish do they stock each year?

a) 2-4 million
b) 10-15 million
c) 26-30 million
d) 40-50 million
e) 75-85 million

Answer

d) On average, the Fish Culture Station raises 40-50 million fry and fingerlings to stock over 200 waterbodies in Saskatchewan each year. Of this, about 97% are Walleye, and about 600,000 are trout fingerlings (Rainbow, Brook, Tiger, Brown, Lake, and Splake). The Station has been operating since 1914.

Bricks and Mortar

Question

The rocket launch pad at Cape Canaveral, Florida used fire bricks produced at this Saskatchewan brick plant:

a) Estevan Coal and Brick Company
b) Bruno Clay Works
c) Saskatoon Brick Yard
d) Claybank Brick Plant
e) Prince Albert Penitentiary Brick Yard

Answer

d) The Claybank Brick Plant shipped fire resistant bricks to Cape Canaveral in the 1970s. Clay used to produce fire bricks at Claybank is considered among the best quality clays in North America for heat resistance. For this reason, Claybank bricks were used at Cape Canaveral where incredible heat is generated during rocket launches.

Fire bricks from Claybank were also used to line fire boxes on locomotives and World War II warships, while facing brick from the plant was used on many prominent buildings such as the Chateau Frontenac hotel in Quebec City, and the Gravelbourg cathedral.

The Claybank Brick Plant is now a National Historic Site.

Question

Name Saskatchewan's oldest existing building.

a) Holy Trinity Anglican Church at Stanley Mission
b) RCMP Chapel in Regina
c) St. Antoine de Padoue Church at Batoche
d) All Saints Anglican Church at Cannington Manor
e) Government House in Battleford

Answer

a) Holy Trinity Anglican Church at Stanley Mission was built between 1854 and 1860, and is now a National Historic Site. Rev. Robert Hunt was responsible for overseeing construction of the massive church which took six years to complete. Local stone and timber were used for the body of the church, while the locks, windows, and window frames, along with 10,000 pieces of stained glass, were shipped from England. The church measures 25 x 10 metres (82 x 33 feet) with a 27-metre (89-foot) steeple.

Holy Trinity Anglican Church.   Karpan Photo

Question

Which church has a stained glass window claimed to be approximately 500 years old?

a)   Holy Trinity Anglican Church in Stanley Mission
b)   St. John's Anglican Cathedral in Saskatoon
c)   Our Lady of Assumption Cathedral in Gravelbourg
d)   All Saints Anglican Church in Watrous
e)   Church of St. Antoine de Padoue at Batoche

Answer

d) All Saints Anglican Church in Watrous claims to have a 2000-piece stained glass window that dates to pre-Reformation times. The story goes that the window was originally installed in the Church of St. John the Baptist in Latton, Wiltshire in England, but was removed for safe keeping during the Civil War between King Charles I and Oliver Cromwell. After peace returned to England, the window was again installed in the church. It remained there until it was replaced by another window.

The daughters of a former vicar at St. John's presented the window to Rev. King of Watrous in 1912, and paid to have it transported to Watrous.

Three tall panels depict St. Peter and St. Paul on either side of the ascended Christ seated on a throne. The Latin inscription *Sedebit rex in aeternum* beneath Christ means "He shall be throned king in eternity". Above the panels, the apostles Matthew, Mark, Luke and John are represented by symbols of a man, a lion, a lamb, and an eagle.

Stained glass window in All Saints Anglican Church, Watrous.

Karpan Photo

Question
Where is the oldest brick building in Saskatchewan?

a) Cumberland House
b) Regina
c) Battleford
d) Claybank
e) Weyburn

Answer
c) The Land Registry Office in Battleford was built in 1877. Located near Government House, it served as a registry office until a new land titles building was constructed in 1908 in downtown Battleford.

Question

Where is the oldest existing Hudson's Bay Company building in Saskatchewan?

a) Ile-à-la-Crosse
b) Cumberland House
c) Pelly
d) Fort Qu'Appelle
e) Green Lake

Answer

d) The annex to the factor's house in Fort Qu'Appelle was built in 1874-75. The building is now part of the Fort Qu'Appelle Museum and Gallery.

Saskatchewan's oldest Hudson's Bay Company building.   Karpan Photo

Question

Which building is said to have the fastest passenger elevators in the province?

a) SaskPower building in Regina
b) Saskatchewan Government Insurance building in Regina
c) CN Towers in Saskatoon
d) Toronto Dominion Bank building in Saskatoon
e) Saskatoon Inn

Answer

b) The elevators at the Saskatchewan Government Insurance building travel at the break-neck speed of 213 metres (700 feet) per minute, which is reportedly the fastest in the province to date. And we all thought that bureaucrats couldn't move quickly!

Question

Built in 1882-83, the RCMP Chapel on the grounds of the RCMP Training Academy is the oldest building in Regina. What was the building used for before becoming a chapel?

a) beer canteen and mess hall
b) barracks
c) storage shed
d) offices
e) commissioner's residence

Answer

a) It was a beer canteen and mess hall. The building was turned into a chapel on the suggestion of Mrs. Herschmer, wife of the commissioner.

Question

Where is Saskatchewan's only full-time operating dance hall that has a horsehair padded floor?

a) Moose Jaw
b) Govan
c) Regina
d) Manitou Beach
e) Battleford

Answer

d) Manitou Beach is home to Danceland, where a horsehair padded floor provides a cushioning effect that helps keep dancers' legs from becoming overly tired. Danceland was built in 1928 on the shore of Little Manitou Lake. It was the dream of Wellington White from Moose Jaw, who, it is said, collected horsehair for two years before building Danceland – enough to fill two railcars. Wrapped in burlap, the horsehair beneath the 464 square metre (5,000 square foot) maple hardwood floor is almost 7.5 cm (3 inches) thick.

Some of Canada's best-known artists have played at Danceland including Don Messer and his Islanders, Wilf Carter, and the Inkspots. Dances and other events continue to be held in the historic dance hall.

Danceland.

Karpan Photo

Question

Which community has a court house patterned after the buildings in colonial Williamsburg, Virginia?

a) Estevan
b) Assiniboia
c) Arcola
d) Yorkton
e) Weyburn

Answer

e) When the Weyburn Court House was built in 1928, colonial revival architecture based on the historic buildings of Williamsburg was in vogue. Provincial architect Maurice Sharon had visited Williamsburg and was influenced by the style. He designed the Weyburn court house with dual chimneys on the sides, shutters, a pronounced columned entrance, central cupola, and a gable roof that gives the appearance of being made of slate, all of which are elements reflecting that style.

Question

Which community has the oldest existing court house in Saskatchewan?

Answer

The Wolseley Court House dates to 1894.

Question

Where is the only two-storey building in Saskatchewan with a complete wrap-around verandah on both stories?

Answer

The Doukhobor Prayer Home in Veregin was built in 1917 and was based on architecture that dates to the mid-1800s in Russia. The upper level served as the residence of Doukhobor leader Peter V. Verigin and his son Peter P. Verigin. It is now part of the National Doukhobor Heritage Village.

Doukhobor Prayer Home, Veregin.   Karpan Photo

Question

This community was headquarters for the only operating chartered bank in Canada to have its head office in Saskatchewan:

a) Weyburn
b) Saskatoon
c) Moose Jaw
d) Prince Albert
e) Regina

Answer

a) The Weyburn Security Bank was chartered in 1911, and operated until it was taken over by the Imperial Bank of Canada in 1931. While other Saskatchewan-based banks received a charter, this was the only one to carry on business. At its height, it had 33 branches throughout southeast Saskatchewan, and even issued its own bank notes.

The original Weyburn Security Bank building, at the corner of Souris Avenue and 3rd Street in downtown Weyburn, is now occupied by the Canadian Imperial Bank of Commerce.

Question

Does anyone in Saskatchewan still live in a sod house?

Answer

Yes. The Addison sod house northeast of Kindersley is the only continuously inhabited sod house known in Saskatchewan, and likely in western Canada. James Addison built the house so well in 1910-11 that it has stood the test of time and is still lived in. The house has walls 1.2 metres (4 feet) thick at the base.

Question

Name the German-born Count whose paintings can be seen in a number of Saskatchewan churches including those at Reward, Muenster, Paradise Hill and St. Walburg.

Answer

Count Berthold von Imhoff was born in Germany in 1868. He immigrated to Canada in 1914, settling in the St. Walburg district. Imhoff was a prolific artist known primarily for his religious paintings which grace many churches throughout Saskatchewan. Other subjects which interested him included still-life, portraits, and animals. Imhoff died in 1939, leaving behind a tremendous legacy of several hundred paintings.

Imhoff's paintings can be seen in the Imhoff Museum near St. Walburg, at the Barr Colony Museum in Lloydminster, as well as in several churches.

Imhoff painting in Holy Rosary Church near Reward.

Karpan Photo

Flying High

Question

Name the Saskatchewan-born pilot who was the RCAF's top ace fighter pilot during World War II.

Answer

Harry Wallace "Wally" McLeod was born in Regina in 1915. He built a reputation as a fighter pilot when he was posted to Malta in 1942, and later when he fought over Belgium and Holland. He is credited with shooting down at least 19 and possibly as many as 21 enemy aircraft.

While McLeod was the RCAF's top pilot, another Canadian, "Buzz" Buerling, flying for Britain's RAF, shot down even more enemy planes. McLeod was obsessed with breaking Buerling's record, and died in the attempt when his Spitfire was shot down in a dog-fight with German fighter planes on September 27, 1944.

Question

Saskatoon and Regina have the two busiest civilian airports in Saskatchewan. Which civilian airport is third busiest?

Answer

La Ronge Airport/Barber Field is third busiest. In addition to scheduled flights, the airport is the base for water-bombers used to fight forest fires.

Question

Which of the following "firsts" in aviation history occurred in Saskatchewan?

a) The first licensed commercial pilot in Canada
b) The first licensed air engineer in Canada
c) The first licensed commercial aircraft in Canada
d) The first licensed air harbour (airport) in Canada
e) The first non-military air ambulance service in North America

Answer

All of the above are Saskatchewan "firsts".

a) On July 31, 1920, Roland Groome from Regina received the first commercial pilot's license in Canada.

b) On April 20, 1920, Robert McCombie, Roland Groome's partner, became the first licensed air engineer in Canada.

c) On April 20, 1920, a Canadian-built Curtiss JN4 biplane became the first licensed commercial aircraft in Canada. It belonged to the Aerial Service Company of Regina, run by Roland Groome and his partner Robert McCombie. This plane was allotted the first registration letters in Canada, G-CAAA. The next letters in the sequence, G-CAAB, were assigned to another Saskatchewan airplane owned by Stan McClelland of Saskatoon.

d) On April 22, 1920, Air Harbour License No. 1 was issued to Regina's Aerial Service Company owned by Groome and McCombie. The airfield was located near the corner of Hill Avenue and Cameron Street.

e) The first non-military air ambulance service in North America was introduced in 1946 by the Saskatchewan government under T.C. Douglas. The first plane, a Norseman, was obtained from Canadian war assets, and fitted for basic ambulance service. The first flight took place on February 3, 1946 when the plane flew from Regina to Liberty to attend to a woman who had suffered a serious diabetic complication.

Roland Groome was the first licensed commercial pilot in Canada.

Saskatchewan Archives R-B 3838

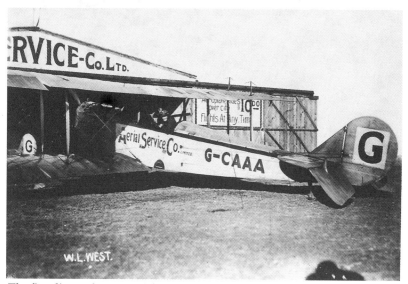

The first licensed commercial aircraft in Canada.
Saskatchewan Archives R-B 3839-1

The first licensed air harbour (airport) in Canada, in Regina.
Saskatchewan Archives R-B 986

Noorduyn Norseman aircraft used for air ambulance in Saskatchewan.
Saskatchewan Archives R-B 2391

Question

Canadian Forces Base 15 Wing Moose Jaw is home to Canada's famous military aerobatic team, the Snowbirds, which perform precision flying demonstrations at events throughout North America. What kind of aircraft do the Snowbirds fly?

a) Avro Arrow
b) CT-114 Tutor
c) CF-104 Starfighter
d) CC-144 Challenger
e) CF-101 Voodoo

Answer

b) The Snowbirds fly CT-114 Tutor aircraft dating to between 1964 and 1967 when the Canadian military purchased 190 Tutor jets. The Snowbirds have 13 planes assigned to them, with 11 travelling to each performance. Their planes have undergone some modifications from the standard aircraft, including the paint scheme, addition of a smoke generating system, and modifications which allow the pilot to fly solo from either seat.

The Snowbirds.　　　　　Courtesy of The Snowbirds, Russ Heinl Photo

Question

What is the maximum speed the Snowbirds' jets fly during their performances?

a) 325 km/hr
b) 475 km/hr
c) 600 km/hr
d) 715 km/hr
e) 775 km/hr

Answer

c) While the speed the jets fly varies throughout the performance, they often reach speeds as high as 600 km/hr. The CT-114 Tutor has a top speed of 763 km/hr.

Question

When the Snowbirds fly their jets in formation, what is the closest they would be to each other?

a) 1.2 metres
b) 2.4 metres
c) 3.5 metres
d) 4.7 metres
e) 5.8 metres

Answer

a) During many of their formations, the jets are often a mere 1.2 metres, or less than four feet apart.

Bridging the Gap

Question

How many bridges cross the South Saskatchewan River in Saskatoon, the "City of Bridges"?

Answer

Seven. Two are railway bridges, the Canadian National Railway Bridge that runs by Diefenbaker Park on the south end of the city, and the Canadian Pacific Railway Bridge that crosses the river near the weir. There are five vehicle bridges: the Idylwyld (freeway) Bridge, Victoria Bridge, Broadway Bridge, University Bridge, and Circle Drive Bridge.

Question

Name the oldest highway bridge still in use in Saskatchewan.

a) Borden Bridge
b) Gabriel's Bridge south of Batoche
c) The old Battleford Bridges on Hwy. #16A
d) St. Louis Bridge
e) Otter Rapids Bridge across the Churchill River

Answer

c) The two bridges on Hwy. #16A across the North Saskatchewan River between Battleford and North Battleford were completed in 1908.

Question

Where is the longest highway bridge in Saskatchewan?

a) Nipawin
b) Cumberland House
c) Saskatchewan Landing
d) Petrofka
e) Outlook

Answer

a) According to Saskatchewan Highways and Transportation, the longest highway bridge in the province is the Nipawin Bridge on Hwy. #55 across the Saskatchewan River, at 466.3 metres (1,530 feet).

Question

How many bridges are there in the provincial highway system?

a) 190
b) 370
c) 580
d) 830
e) 910

Answer

d) According to Saskatchewan Highways and Transportation, there are 830 bridges in the provincial highway system.

Question

How many ferries operate on the North and South Saskatchewan River systems in Saskatchewan?

Answer

Twelve. The Cecil, Wingard, and Paynton Ferries operate on the North Saskatchewan River. The Weldon, Fenton, St. Laurent, Hague, Clarkboro, Lancer, Lemsford, and Estuary Ferries operate on the South Saskatchewan River. The Riverhurst Ferry crosses Lake Diefenbaker, a trip of 2.2 km.

Ferries have been used in Saskatchewan since the fur trade days. The first ferries to provide regular service were established at St. Laurent and Batoche in the early 1870s. Saskatchewan's most famous ferry operator was Gabriel Dumont, Louis Riel's military leader in the 1885 Northwest Rebellion. Prior to the uprising, Dumont operated a ferry across the South Saskatchewan River near present day Gabriel's Bridge south of Batoche. Ferries continue to be important for travellers, local residents, and farmers. Service is offered as soon as the rivers become ice free, and continues until freeze-up.

St. Laurent ferry.

Karpan Photo

Question

Where is the longest wooden trestle bridge still standing in Saskatchewan?

Answer

The McCloy Creek railway trestle bridge just west of Meskanaw on Hwy. #41 is over a quarter mile long and 15.25 metres (50 feet) high. Built by the CNR in 1930, it was originally 381 metres (1,251 feet) long, but problems with shifting banks made it necessary to extend the bridge to 432 metres (1,417 feet) in 1932. The amazing part of this bridge is that it is made almost entirely of wood.

The bridge was part of a CNR line that ran to Hudson Bay where traffic could be funnelled to the Hudson Bay Railway and the Port of Churchill. The bridge was not only difficult to build, it was also a challenge to maintain because of the soft, marshy valley floor, and shifting valley banks. The rail line was abandoned in the early 1980s, but the massive wooden trestle is still standing.

McCloy Creek Bridge.   Karpan Photo

Question

Where was the first paved road in Saskatchewan?

Answer

A short strip was constructed in 1928 east of Regina en route to Pilot Butte.

Question

Approximately how many scrap tires are generated each year in Saskatchewan?

a) .5 million
b) .75 million
c) 1 million
d) 1.6 million
e) 2.1 million

Answer

c) Each year, approximately 1 million used tires are generated in the province, which works out to be almost one tire per person.

Tires are made to last, and can take up a lot of space in landfills. That's where the Saskatchewan Scrap Tire Corporation comes in. Formed in 1996, the agency coordinates recycling tires into products such as planters, playground equipment, flooring, and even alternative fuels. Fees collected on new tires are used for the recycling program. Since the recycling program was started, tire dumping in landfills has declined markedly.

Question

Saskatchewan has more roads than any other province or territory in Canada. How many kilometres of roads are there?

a) 130,000
b) 156,000
c) 187,000
d) 225,000
e) 250,000

Answer

c) According to Saskatchewan Highways and Transportation, there are 187,300 km of roads in the province – 26,200 km of highways and 161,100 km of municipal roads. Municipal roads can be broken down into 1,600 km of paved municipal roads, 114,000 km of gravel roads that include farm and home access roads, and 45,500 km of field access roads, which may be either gravel or dirt.

Question

How many vehicles are registered in Saskatchewan?

a) 500,000
b) 725,000
c) 800,000
d) 950,000
e) 1,200,000

Answer

c) According to Saskatchewan Government Insurance, there were 834,547 registered vehicles as of the end of 2002. That works out to be approximately one vehicle per person aged 15 and over.

Monumental Musings

Question

Where is Saskatchewan's only lighthouse?

a) Lampman
b) Cochin
c) Reindeer Lake
d) Spy Hill
e) Lake Athabasca

Answer

b) The resort village of Cochin is home to the only lighthouse in Saskatchewan. Built atop Pirot Hill overlooking Jackfish Lake, the lighthouse stands 11.5 metres (38 feet) tall, and can be reached by climbing 153 steps. In true lighthouse-fashion, it even has a rotating beacon that is visible for miles around.

The lighthouse was the dream of Cochin resident Tom Archdekin, who spearheaded the idea as a tourism project in 1988. With support from village council, and especially from the Pirot family who allowed the lighthouse to be built on their land, the project went ahead the following year.

Unlike lighthouses by the sea that warn of dangerous reefs or peninsulas, the Cochin lighthouse beckons visitors to have a closer look at this community on Hwy. #4 north of North Battleford.

Question

Where can you see a 9.75-metre (32-foot) "bunnock", which is a representation of a horse ankle bone?

a) Maidstone
b) Macklin
c) Morse
d) Meskanaw
e) Melville

Answer

b) Just outside the town of Macklin at the junction of Hwys. #13 and #41, is the giant white bunnock built of steel pipes, wire, and fibreglass. It was enlarged 98 times the size of an actual horse ankle bone. In the summer the big bunnock serves as a tourist booth for Macklin and area.

Bunnock was introduced to Canada by Russian German immigrants. It is believed the game originated in Siberia when soldiers posted there were looking for something to do to alleviate boredom. Since the bones of horses were plentiful, the soldiers invented a game where the object was to knock down the bunnocks of the opposing team. Sounds simple enough, all right, but rules about which ones have to be knocked over first make the game extremely challenging.

It didn't take long for bunnock to catch on in Macklin, where the annual World Championship Bunnock Tournament draws teams from many countries.

Bunnock tourist information booth near Macklin.   Karpan Photo

Question

Where can you find an 8-metre (26-foot) high lily?

a) Kelliher
b) Eatonia
c) Ponteix
d) Parkside
e) Moosomin

Answer

d) The Flaming Red Giant is a statue of an 8-metre (26-foot) lily, located in Parkside along Hwy. #40. It was built in recognition of Dr. A. J. (Bert) Porter and his many horticultural achievements. Dr. Porter established Honeywood Nursery just outside Parkside, and over many years became famous for breeding and growing a variety of hardy lilies that won national and international awards.

Question

Where can you see a 9.4-metre (31-foot) pea plant?

a) St. Isidore de Bellevue
b) St. Benedict
c) St. Gregor
d) St. Walburg
e) St. Louis

Answer

a) The giant pea sculpture is in St. Isidore de Bellevue, and was chosen as the symbol to represent the community because peas and other legume crops have been grown in the area for several years. Belle Pulse is one of the village's main businesses, a seed cleaning and processing plant that can split peas, and prepare and ship chick peas, lentils, yellow peas, green peas, and red peas that are popular in Asia. The restaurant at Le Rendez-vous Cultural Centre in Bellevue serves homemade pea soup prepared from locally grown peas.

Question

Which community has a 6.1-metre (20-foot) high statue of a whooping crane?

a) Wadena
b) Lucky Lake
c) Paradise Hill
d) Springside
e) Govan

Answer

e) Govan. Whooping cranes are frequent visitors to nearby Last Mountain Lake during their migration.

Question

Which community claims to have the world's largest tomahawk ?

a)   Cut Knife
b)   Yellow Grass
c)   La Ronge
d)   Spiritwood
e)   Fort Qu'Appelle

Answer

a) Cut Knife claims to have the largest tomahawk in the world. Located in Tomahawk Park by the campground, the monument was built in 1971 to symbolize friendship among communities in the Cut Knife region.

The tomahawk handle is a fir log measuring 16.4 metres (54 feet) long and weighing 6 tonnes. The head, constructed of reinforced fibreglass, measures 5.5 metres (18 feet) long, 2.75 metres (9 feet) in diameter, and weighs 1,134 kg (2,500 pounds). The tomahawk rests on a precast concrete tipi.

Tomahawk at Cut Knife.   Karpan Photo

Question

Which Saskatchewan community welcomes you with an 8.5-metre (28-foot) high oil can?

a) Langenburg
b) Spy Hill
c) Rocanville
d) Churchbridge
e) Wawota

Answer

c) Ernie Symons' design of the pump oiler put the town of Rocanville on the map. After listening to complaints from farmers about oil cans that weren't able to reach out of the way places, Ernie decided to improve the design of a pump oiler by adding a thumb lever, a handle, and a moving spout attached to the plunger. His new oiler was capable of shooting oil over 4.5 metres (15 feet)!

Ernie began production in 1924 with two dozens oilers. Production rose to 400 units the following year, and 3,500 in 1926. Demonstrations at major fairs across western Canada helped boost sales, as did orders from defence contracts during the Second World War. The Symons Oiler became an indispensable tool not only with Canadians, but in many countries around the world.

At its height, the Symons Metalworkers plant turned out 65,000 units in 1944. In 50 years of production, some 1.5 million oilers were made in eight different sizes. Since Ernie's death in 1989, the factory has been closed.

In 1973, the town paid tribute to Ernie for 50 years of continuous production by constructing the huge scale model of the Symons Oiler.

Model of Symons Oiler, Rocanville

Karpan Photo

Question

Which community has a monument with a $1 coin that is 1.8 metres (6 feet) in diameter?

a) Langenburg
b) Churchbridge
c) Bredenbury
d) Esterhazy
e) Stockholm

Answer

b) Rita Swanson of Churchbridge submitted the winning design for the commemorative $1 coin marking Canada's 125th birthday in 1992. Her art work incorporated the Canadian flag, children, and the Parliament Buildings. On June 29, 1993, exactly one year after the coin was released by the Royal Canadian Mint, the bronze coin monument made by Saskatchewan artist Bill Epp was unveiled in Churchbridge.

Question

The town of Davidson has a huge coffee pot standing 7.3 metres (24 feet) high. If this pot were filled with coffee, how many 8-ounce cups would it hold?

a) 40,000
b) 80,000
c) 110,000
d) 130,000
e) 150,000

Answer

e) The gigantic coffee pot would hold approximately 150,000 cups of coffee, according to a spokesperson for the town of Davidson. The colorful pot was built in 1996 to symbolize Davidson's popularity as a coffee-stop, as the town is located midway between Saskatoon and Regina, and also midway between Saskatoon and Moose Jaw.

Davidson's coffee pot.   Karpan Photo

Question

Where can you see what is believed to be the world's largest replica of a moose?

a) Moose Mountain
b) Moose Factory
c) Moose Head Inn at Kenosee Lake
d) Moose Jaw
e) Moosomin

Answer

d) Moose Jaw claims to be home to the world's largest moose which stands beside the Trans-Canada Highway. "Mac the Moose" contains 9,070 kg of steel and concrete and stands 9.75 metres (32 feet) high. Officially unveiled on May 20, 1984, the city's mascot was named "Mac" after the late alderman Les McKenzie.

"Mac" the Moose.

Karpan Photo

Question

Where can you see what is claimed to be the world's largest grasshopper?

a) Meacham
b) Blaine Lake
c) Unity
d) Wilkie
e) Shellbrook

Answer

d) Wilkie claims to have the world's largest grasshopper, nicknamed "Hoppy". Built of cedar in 1993 by local craftsman Byron Hansen, Hoppy weighs 1,814 kg (4,000 pounds), is 6 meters (20 feet) long, 1.8 metres (6 feet) wide, and 4.5 metres (15 feet) high.

"Hoppy".   Karpan Photo

Question

Near which community can you find the Great Wall of Saskatchewan?

a) St. Walburg
b) Waldheim
c) Waldron
d) Rockglen
e) Smiley

Answer

e) The Great Wall of Saskatchewan is 3 km west of Smiley. Made entirely of stones, the wall is about 1 km long, 3 metres wide, and 2 metres high. It doesn't keep anything in or out, and has no practical purpose other than artistic expression. The wall was built by Albert "Stonewall" Johnson, a farmer who began clearing stones from his land some 30 years ago. Rather than simply dumping them in a pile, Albert spent three decades carefully arranging the rocks into a wall, without using cement or mortar. People often ask why Albert decided to build the wall, but the better question might be, why not?

Albert Johnson and the "Great Wall".   Karpan Photo

Question

Which community has a 7.7-metre (25-foot) statue of a woman in traditional Ukrainian dress?

a) Kamsack
b) Canora
c) Yorkton
d) Hafford
e) Lloydminster

Answer

b) Canora's statue, named Lesia, stands at the south entrance to town. Reflecting the Ukrainian and Eastern European heritage of Canora's residents, Lesia carries a tray with bread and salt, which are customary gifts to visitors.

The statue was constructed by Canora residents Nicholas and Orest Lewchuck, and was installed in 1980.

Karpan Photo

Question

Where can you see a 6.7-metre (22-foot) model of a Dutch windmill?

a) Meota
b) Preeceville
c) Langenburg
d) Windthorst
e) Edam

Answer

e) Edam's windmill commemorates the heritage of Dutch settlers who moved to this district just after the turn of the century. Many came from Edam, Holland, and named the

settlement after their home town. The windmill was built in 1980 on the outskirts of the village to celebrate the 75th anniversary of the province.

Karpan Photo

Official Stuff

Question

What is Saskatchewan's official bird emblem?

a) ruffed grouse
b) sharp-tailed grouse
c) sage grouse
d) great horned owl
e) black-capped chickadee

Answer

b) The sharp-tailed grouse was chosen as the provincial bird emblem in 1945. Sharp-tailed grouse are common on the prairies, especially in sheltered thickets, aspen bluffs, and sandy hills.

The birds are known for their colorful courtship displays. On early spring mornings, often before the snow has left, males begin to congregate at their traditional dancing grounds known as leks. Their displays attract females who come to watch them stamp the ground in their unique dancing manoeuvres which involve plenty of turning and cooing to impress the females. With their wings extended and their purple neck patches inflated, the males continue displaying until sunrise when the birds generally disperse.

Question

Saskatchewan's provincial motto in Latin is *Multis E Gentibus Vires*. What does this mean?

a) From many peoples, strength.
b) From prairie to pine.
c) Prosperity from a gentle land.
d) Land of the plains bison.
e) Cold enough for you?

Answer

a) "From many peoples, strength" is the provincial motto, referring to the many varied backgrounds of Saskatchewan's people.

Question

Name Saskatchewan's official mineral.

a) uranium
b) sylvite (potash)
c) gold
d) coal
e) copper

Answer

b) Sylvite (potash) was chosen as Saskatchewan's official mineral in 1996.

Question

What is Saskatchewan's floral emblem?

a) lily of the valley
b) western red lily
c) tiger lily
d) dandelion
e) crocus

Answer

b) The western red lily was adopted as the provincial floral emblem in 1941. The bright orange flowers are often found in road-side ditches, meadows, and open woods. Picking the flowers causes the plant to die.

Western red lily.   Karpan Photo

Question

What is Saskatchewan's provincial tree?

a) white birch
b) jack pine
c) balsam poplar
d) white spruce
e) trembling aspen

Answer

a) The white birch was selected as Saskatchewan's provincial tree in 1988. Another name for the white birch is "paper birch", as its bark peels in thin papery layers.

It is common in the boreal forest, and prefers moist soil. While most prevalent in the north, a large stand of birch is also found in Moose Mountain Provincial Park in southern Saskatchewan, where the highlands provide a cool and moist habitat.

Native peoples used birch trees for dozens of purposes. The strong bark was used to make canoes, baskets and other containers. The hard wood was used for tipi poles, racks for smoking meat or fish, snowshoes, sleds, as well as canoe paddles, hammer handles, and arrows. Dry strips of the outer bark make excellent kindling.

Question

Which three animals are depicted on Saskatchewan's Coat of Arms?

a) lion
b) moose
c) gopher
d) deer
e) bear
f) beaver
g) coyote

Answer

a, d, f) The top of the Coat of Arms has a beaver with a crown. The beaver is holding a western red lily, Saskatchewan's floral emblem. To the left of the shield is a lion and to the right is a white-tailed deer. Both are wearing collars of Prairie Indian beadwork.

Saskatchewan Coat of Arms.

Question

Saskatchewan is the only province in Canada not to go on and off Daylight Saving Time.

a) True
b) False

Answer

a) True. Saskatchewan stays on Central Standard time year round. We like to think of Saskatchewan as the one point of stability in a country that can't make up its mind what time it is.

Question

Most Saskatchewan residents consider English to be their mother tongue. The four most prevalent "mother tongue languages" after English are French, German, Ukrainian and Cree. Put these languages in order from most common to least common.

a) French, German, Ukrainian, Cree
b) French, Ukrainian, Cree, German
c) German, Ukrainian, French, Cree
d) German, Cree, Ukrainian, French
e) Ukrainian, German, French, Cree

Answer

d) According to Statistics Canada data from the last census (2001), 827,351 Saskatchewan residents indicated English as their mother tongue. German was second with 34,340, Cree third with 24,040, Ukrainian fourth with 21,040, and French fifth with 19,525.

Also from Parkland Publishing...

Saskatchewan Scenic Secrets *by Robin and Arlene Karpan*

See Saskatchewan as you have never seen it before. With 145 stunning colour photographs and informative commentary, award-winning writers and photographers, Robin and Arlene Karpan, take you on a visual journey through Saskatchewan, from the deep south to the far north, to where the beauty of nature takes centre stage. Discover a landscape rife with superlatives – the largest tracts of grasslands on the Great Plains, the largest sand dunes in Canada, wetlands of international significance, northern lakelands, and wild pristine rivers.

$34.95 • Hard cover, full colour • 11 x 8 ½ • 128 pages
145 colour photos • ISBN 0-9683579-3-8

Saskatchewan Trails – A Guide to Nature Walks and Easy Hikes (2nd Edition) *by Robin and Arlene Karpan*

Saskatchewan Trails guides you on over 100 nature trails through the province's diverse landscapes, from prairie grasslands to aspen parkland, boreal forest, shield country, badlands, lakelands, and river valleys.

$19.95 • Soft cover, perfect bound • 5 ½ x 8 ½ • 288 pages
91 b&w photos • 90 maps • ISBN 0-9683579-4-6

Northern Sandscapes – Exploring Saskatchewan's Athabasca Sand Dunes *by Robin and Arlene Karpan*

The Athabasca Sand Dunes are like nowhere else on Earth – a desert-like environment seemingly misplaced in the northern forest. Join writers and photographers Robin and Arlene Karpan on an exciting canoe journey through this stunning wilderness.

$29.95 • Soft cover, perfect bound • 8 ½ x 11 • 128 pages
115 colour photos • ISBN 0-9683579-0-3

Western Canadian Farm Trivia Challenge
by Robin and Arlene Karpan

It's time to have some fun with farming. Which country is the biggest export market for our wheat? (The answer may surprise you.) Do you know how much a cow pie weighs, how many seeds there are in a bushel of canola, or how far a honey bee would have to fly to collect enough nectar for a pound of honey? Can you name the prairie community that built a bronze statue to honor a pig that escaped from the abattoir? How much does a farmer get paid for the barley that goes into one bottle of beer? All is revealed in more than 325 questions and answers in *Western Canadian Farm Trivia Challenge*.

$14.95 • *Soft cover, perfect bound* • *5 ½ x 8 ½* • *192 pages*
66 b&w photos • *ISBN 0-9683579-5-4*

Books available at better bookstores, or contact Parkland Publishing at 306-242-7731, www.parklandpublishing.com

About the Authors

Robin and Arlene Karpan are writers and photographers based in Saskatoon, Saskatchewan. They are the authors of award-winning and bestselling books, and have contributed to more than 100 publications around the world.

PARKLAND
PUBLISHING

Order Form

Parkland Publishing
501 Mount Allison Place
Saskatoon, Sask.
Canada S7H 4A9

Phone: 306-242-7731
Fax: 306-242-7731
E-mail: info@parklandpublishing.com

For additional copies of *Saskatchewan Trivia Challenge,* contact your nearest bookseller or send a cheque or money order to Parkland Publishing.

_____ copies @ $14.95 each   _____

Shipping and handling – add $3.00 for the first book, and $1.00 for each additional book   _____

Subtotal   _____

Add 7% GST (GST# 117060830)   _____

Total   _____

Please make cheques payable to Parkland Publishing.

Ship to:

Name   _____

Address _____

_____

Postal Code _____   Phone _____

Please contact Parkland Publishing for special pricing on large orders or for orders outside Canada.

Prices and shipping charges subject to change without notice.